KETO FOR **vegans**

BOOK 1

over 30 nutritious vegan ketogenic recipes
& a 5-week meal plan

HEATHER VARALEAU

Blue Spatula Press

THIS BOOK **belongs to:**

____

First published in 2023 by Blue Spatula Press

Visit the author's website at keto4vegans.com.

ISBN-13: 978-1-7384415-0-1 (print - color)
ISBN-13: 978-1-7384415-2-5 (print - black & white)
ISBN-13: 978-1-7384415-1-8 (ebook)

The author is not a licensed practitioner, physician, or medical professional and offers no medical diagnoses, treatments, suggestions, or counseling. The information presented herein has not been evaluated by the U.S. Food and Drug Administration or any other equivalent national or international authority, and is not intended to diagnose, treat, cure, or prevent any disease. Full medical clearance from a licensed physician should be obtained before beginning or modifying any diet, exercise, or lifestyle program, and physicians should be informed of all nutritional changes.

The author of this book claims no responsibility to any person or entity for any liability, loss, or damage caused or alleged to be caused directly or indirectly as a result of the use, application, or interpretation of the information presented herein.

Cover design, interior design, and photography by Heather Varaleau

First edition 2023

TABLE OF **contents**

SPECIAL **thanks to**

First and foremost, I would like to thank my mother, from whom my culinary skills, inclination towards healthful eating, and passion for cooking have come. I love you. Next, I would like to thank Maddy, the creator of the VKMS Facebook group, my co-modmin Vanessa, and all of the VKMS group members who shared their positive energy, and especially those who encouraged me to write a cookbook. It is because of you that this book exists. Last but not least, I would like to thank the many friends who offered their support and taste-testing services. To name a few, Haris, who has always encouraged me to pursue my passions and celebrated my successes, Adam and Maria, who always made a point of providing detailed and constructive feedback, Frank, whose freezer may still contain some of my many recipe-testing leftovers, Jason, whose list of my top 5 creations has far exceeded its numerical boundaries, Dave, who first suggested I explore photography, Karen, without whom the first draft would likely have never been printed, Amanda, who provided valuable design feedback, Aaron, whose editing suggestions to meet nutritional needs with copper wiring and bananas, due to space constraints, did not make it into the final draft, and Dubravka, whose podcasts kept me company, held me accountable, lauded my accomplishments, and cheered me on.

ABOUT THE **author** (that's me)

I grew up in small town western Canada. My mom milled fresh whole wheat flour for our bread and my dad took great pride in the vastness of his woodpiles and the precision with which he plowed the snow from the long driveway that led to our beautiful home nestled in the forest. We had our own potato patch and clucking chickens ran amok. My mom took great care in what she fed her family, and our food often came from regional farms and neighboring gardens; the white sugar my sister and I finally badgered her into buying as teens was stored in a yellow 1960s Tupperware canister labelled "white death".

My mom is an excellent cook and my sister and I spent countless hours of our childhood in the kitchen alongside her, learning and making a nuisance of ourselves. It's no surprise that we both grew up with a passion for cooking and an affinity for healthy eating.

A number of years ago, I stumbled upon the keto diet and became quite enthralled. However, I soon found that after having spent a number of years following an increasingly *reducetarian* diet, my food choices had starkly reversed course. Then, I ran across a Facebook group focusing on vegan keto, and that's where the story of this book begins.

This book, a passion project, combines my love of cooking and my knack for rising above unique creative challenges with my interests in nutritious foods and reducing the impact human food choices have on the planet and all those who inhabit it. I hope my book finds you well, that the pages within it bring you joy, and that the recipes leave you nourished.

VEGAN KETO **basics**

WHAT IS A KETOGENIC DIET?

Under typical modern-day dietary conditions, the human body primarily uses carbohydrates, broken down into glucose, as its main source of fuel. However, a ketogenic diet is a dietary approach that significantly restricts carbohydrates, leading to a reduced supply of glucose for energy production. In the absence of sufficient glucose, the body shifts its metabolism to utilize fat, specifically fatty acids, as its primary fuel source. This metabolic state is known as ketosis. When the body is in ketosis, the liver produces molecules called ketones, which are then also used as a source of fuel. It is from this production of ketones that the ketogenic diet derives its name.

MACRONUTRIENTS: CARBOHYDRATES

Carbohydrates, or *carbs*, are one of three main macronutrients, alongside protein and fat. Carbohydrates are found in foods primarily as sugars, starch, and fiber. However, sugar alcohols and allulose are also carbohydrates. Sugar alcohols occur naturally in very small amounts in some plant foods, but are most abundant as sugar substitutes. Allulose is also a sugar substitute. These sweeteners are discussed in more detail on page 8.

Carbohydrates can be broadly categorized as either digestible or indigestible. A ketogenic diet focuses on limiting the consumption of digestible carbohydrates, or *net carbs*. Net carbs are the total carbohydrates minus the indigestible carbohydrates. Indigestible carbohydrates include fiber and allulose, and may include sugar alcohols, in whole or in part. Digestible carbohydrates are sugars, both naturally occurring and added, and starches.

Carbohydrates are abundant in plant foods, making a vegan ketogenic diet uniquely challenging. Limiting the consumption of digestible carbohydrates means avoiding or significantly reducing the consumption of sugars, syrups, grains, pseudograins (e.g. quinoa), most legumes, cashews, high-sugar fruits, and starchy root vegetables (e.g. potatoes). Nutritional needs must be met with the low-sugar low-starch food options that remain, namely vegetables, mushrooms, nuts and seeds (most types), low-sugar fruits, soy and lupini beans (and their derivatives), and products made from pea protein isolate. See the food list on page 14 for further guidance.

The degree of carbohydrate restriction required to maintain ketosis varies from person to person. Typically, maintaining ketosis requires limiting net carb intake to an amount between 20 and 50 grams, an amount referred to as one's *carb limit*. When determining your carb limit, take into consideration not only how restrictive you need to be to maintain ketosis, but also whether it's necessary for you to maintain ketosis consistently throughout the day in order to meet your health goals and what amount of restriction is practical, healthful, and sustainable for you as an individual.

If your priority is to consistently maintain ketosis without testing for ketones, adhering to a net carb limit of 20 to 30 grams is likely to achieve this objective. Some individuals, especially those who lead a highly active lifestyle, may find they are able to maintain ketosis with a higher carb limit. Determining this limit would require ketone testing, which is discussed in more detail on the following page.

Maintaining ketosis each and every moment of the day may not be required to meet your health goals, and an unnecessarily low carb limit may actually hinder your ability to adhere to the diet and to meet your overall nutritional needs. A carb limit at the higher end of the range allows for the consumption of a wider variety of foods, a more abundant vegetable intake, and, in all likelihood, a more enjoyable, well-rounded, and sustainable eating experience.

Significant dietary changes should be discussed with a healthcare professional, and this is especially true if embarking on a new diet for medical purposes. A well-informed registered dietician can provide personalized guidance on whether and how to adopt a vegan ketogenic diet based on your specific circumstances.

MACRONUTRIENTS: PROTEIN

Protein serves numerous functions in the human body and is crucial for overall health. In a non-ketogenic vegan diet or a non-vegan ketogenic diet, obtaining sufficient protein is usually not a concern. However, the limitations of a vegan ketogenic diet present a unique challenge in finding protein-rich food options.

On a vegan ketogenic diet, primary sources of protein may include soybeans and soy products like tofu and soymilk, lupini beans and lupin products like lupin flour and ground lupin, products made with pea protein isolate like pea milk and pea-based textured vegetable protein (TVP), nuts and seeds (especially chia, flax, hemp, and pumpkin), peanuts, nutritional yeast flakes, leafy greens (especially spinach), certain non-leafy vegetables like asparagus and broccolini, mushrooms, protein powder, and select low-carb plant-based meats. While nearly all foods contain some protein, most vegetable and fruit intake will make only a limited contribution to meeting your overall protein needs, especially if your carb limit is on the low end of the range. Produce items that are particularly high in protein relative to their net carb content are marked with a pink heart (♥) in the food list on page 14.

Creating a nutritious and sustainable vegan ketogenic diet can be challenging, and those unable or unwilling to consume multiple primary protein sources, may find that embarking on a vegan ketogenic diet is unrealistic and nutritionally ill-advised. Note that individuals not consuming legumes may require a well-formulated protein powder or supplement in order to meet their lysine needs.

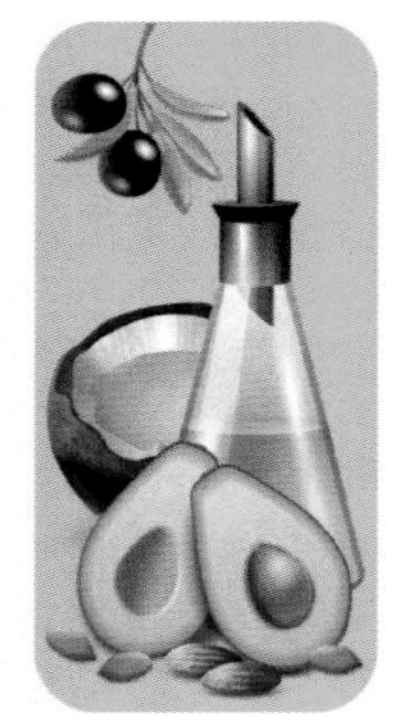

Macronutrients: Fat

When carbohydrates are restricted, another macronutrient needs to provide the necessary calories in its place. Thus, a ketogenic diet is inherently a high-fat diet unless one's calorie requirement is especially low. Nuts and seeds (including their butters and flours), avocados, and coconut are notably abundant sources of fat. Incorporating these foods into your diet, as well as using oils in dressings, sauces, and for cooking, can easily increase the fat content of your meals.

Dietary fats are a topic of ongoing debate and disagreement within the diet, nutrition, and medical communities. Researchers, medical professionals, self-appointed experts, influencers, and enthusiasts hold differing opinions on which fats are considered healthful or detrimental. While trans fats are universally regarded as harmful and monounsaturated fats are generally recognized as beneficial, there remains debate around the health effects of high saturated fat consumption and the inclusion of certain oils in the diet. The fats you choose to include in your diet are at your own discretion.

Monounsaturated fats are found in high concentrations in most nuts, pumpkin and sesame seeds, peanuts, avocados, olives, and oils derived from these sources. Canola oil is high in both mono and polyunsaturated fats, and its healthfulness is debated by some.

Polyunsaturated fats exist in walnuts, most seeds, and oils derived from these sources. In addition, they are particularly abundant in corn, cottonseed, safflower, and soybean oils, commonly referred to as *vegetable oils* or *industrial seed oils*. These oils are an area of contention, with some claiming that they are harmful to health.

Saturated fats are prevalent in coconut, coconut oil, palm oil, and cocoa/cacao butter. High saturated fat consumption may be of concern for those with, or at risk of developing, high cholesterol.

Trans fats are found in partially hydrogenated oils, often used in margarines and vegetable shortenings, and are known to affect health negatively. It is advisable to minimize trans fat consumption.

Omega-3s

Omega-3 polyunsaturated fatty acids are essential fatty acids and have been associated with numerous health benefits. There are three main types: eicosapentaenoic acid (EPA), docosahexaenoic acid (DHA), and alpha-linolenic acid (ALA). EPA and DHA are primarily animal-based, with limited and variable amounts found only in certain seaweeds and algaes. Conversely, ALA is plant-based and plentiful in chia seeds, flax seeds, hemp hearts, and walnuts. The body must convert ALA to EPA and DHA for use, and the conversion rate is limited, inefficient, and variable. While it is unlikely that one will become Omega-3 deficient if consuming only ALA, taking an algae-oil supplement may provide health benefits.

Testing Ketone Levels

There are three methods for testing ketone levels: urine, breath, and blood. Among these, urine and blood testing are the most common and products are readily available in pharmacies or online. Blood testing is the more accurate, and the more expensive, option.

Urine test strips detect concentrations of excreted excess acetoacetate, a type of ketone. They do not directly measure the amount of ketones circulating within, or utilized by, the body. While urine tests can provide an indication of ketone production, they are imprecise. The results of urine analysis should be taken with a grain of salt as they may not accurately reflect blood ketone levels.

Blood ketone measurements require specific ketone testing strips and a corresponding reading device called a ketone meter or ketone monitor. This testing method is similar to the one used by diabetics to test blood glucose levels. By pricking your finger, you can measure the level of beta-hydroxybutyrate (BHB), another type of ketone, in your blood. Levels between 0.5 and 3.0 mmol are typically considered indicative of nutritional ketosis. Levels above 3.0 mmol may occur during prolonged fasting or when employing a ketogenic diet for specific therapeutic/medical purposes, but excessively high blood ketone levels are not required for nutritional ketosis and, if sustained, may be cause for concern.

Ketone breath analyzers, which can be purchased online, measure the levels of acetone, a third type of ketone, in your breath. These devices operate by simply blowing into them. While convenient and non-invasive, breath analysis is generally considered less accurate and precise than blood analysis. Breath acetone levels are an indirect measure of the amount of ketones circulating in the body and may not directly correlate with the concentration in the blood.

Unless using a ketogenic diet for therapeutic purposes, testing ketones is not a requirement. It can be costly, and a fixation on ketone levels can impact one's overall well-being. If you are strictly adhering to a ketogenic diet, you are likely in ketosis. However, there are a few other signs you could look for to indicate you are in, or entering, ketosis. During the initial adaptation period, you may notice a significant loss of water weight (5 to 10 pounds [2 to 5 kg]) and subsequent increased urination. You may also experience symptoms of keto flu, which is described in more detail on page 11. Other changes that may present in the early stages, and may endure, are reduced hunger and appetite, increased energy levels, heightened mental clarity, reduced water retention, less bloating, and changes in breath and body odor.

Finding and Tracking Your Macros

Macros is short for macronutrients. *Your macros* typically refers to your personal calorie requirement and the breakdown of protein, fat, and net carbs that you intend to consume in order to meet this requirement. Individual macros will vary depending on factors such as gender, age, activity level, and health and fitness goals.

Various online calculators can help you determine your ideal macros. The Keto Calculator at www.ruled.me/keto-calculator/ is one such option. Web or app-based tracking programs, like Cronometer, usually include their own calculators. For those who prefer to use data calculated elsewhere, these programs often allow for manual input of calorie and macronutrient targets.

Tracking your macros involves recording the macronutrient and calorie content of the foods you consume. This allows you to assess whether you are meeting your targets, or staying within certain limitations, and make adjustments to your diet if needed. While tracking is not essential, it can provide valuable insights and help you meet your nutritional needs and objectives. It's important to be mindful of the time commitment and possible impact on mental health that tracking can have. Striking a balance between helpful tracking and potential drawbacks is integral to overall well-being.

While tracking can be accomplished through various methods, purpose-built tracking programs are a great tool. These specialized programs offer the convenience of setting up a personal profile with personalized calorie and macronutrient targets, and come equipped with a comprehensive database of foods from which you can select items to add to your daily diary. Once selected, the program automatically calculates the total calories and nutrients consumed, allowing you to easily compare your intake with your targets. Users can add new food items to the database, and many programs allow users to build and save custom recipes.

Food data in tracking programs typically comes from two sources: national databases, such as the NCCDB (Nutrition Coordinating Center Food & Nutrient Database) or the USDA (United States Food and Drug Administration), and product labels. Data from the former is derived from lab analyses and research papers, and tends to be the most comprehensive, while data from the latter is much more limited, less precise, and for the most part added to the database by program users. Label data is typically rounded, and in some countries, the use of small serving sizes may paint an inaccurate picture of a food's actual macronutrient content. Despite this, label data may be more accurate for processed items, especially condiments, sauces, and ingredient-dense products.

Regardless of source, data in tracking programs may contain discrepancies. It is prudent to compare your labels to database entries when making selections, particularly for user-added or brand-specific data. For whole foods and foods with minimal and primarily whole-food ingredients, using national lab-analyzed data will provide you with a better picture of your overall nutrient intake.

In my experience, there are some common whole-food items for which the national data consistently and significantly differs from product label data. In such cases, using label data, or a combination of label and national data, may be preferable. Notable items are agar agar, canned tomatoes, canned coconut milk, chia seeds, hemp hearts, pumpkin seeds, soymilk, sunflower seed butter, and tofu. Other common items that less consistently show significant discrepancies are bullion cubes, mayonnaise, oil-roasted peanuts, soy sauce, tahini, and tamari. There is no national lab-analyzed data for brined lupini beans, though data for cooked beans does exist.

To combine the benefits of label and national data, some programs, like Cronometer, allow users to save a copy of, and edit, a database entry. This enables the user to replace applicable fields in a national database entry with the data from a product label, thus creating a custom entry that is both product specific and comprehensive.

Tracking can be burdensome. However, there are several ways to make the process more manageable. Possibilities include batch cooking, eating the same meals frequently, following a meal plan, in-advance tracking, and periodic tracking. In-advance tracking entails dedicating a short period of time each day or week to planning out and inputting the foods you will consume in the day or week ahead. In-advance tracking saves time while also ensuring your daily nutrition targets will be met. Periodic tracking refers to tracking initially to get a feel for the parameters of your new diet and then only every now and then when you wish to introduce new foods or feel you may have veered off course.

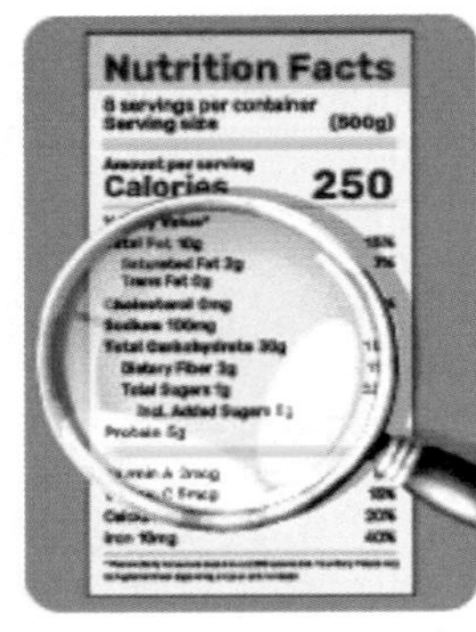

Reading labels

Label formats vary by country, but some generalizations can be made. In Canada and the US, labels list total carbohydrates, with dietary fiber, sugars, and sugar alcohols indented on separate lines directly underneath. The food's net carbs are determined by subtracting the fiber and sugar alcohols (if applicable) from the total carbohydrates. For example, if a product has 10g total carbohydrates, 5g fiber, and 2g sugar alcohols, it has 3g net carbs. Not all products contain sugar alcohols, so they will not appear on all labels.

In other parts of the world, labels typically list carbohydrates with the fiber already deducted. The carbohydrates and fiber will be listed on separate lines, and the fiber will not be indented. If the product does not contain any sugar alcohols (aka polyols), then the carbohydrate number given is the net carbs. When polyols are present, how they are listed may vary. If polyols are given on an indented line directly beneath the carbohydrates, subtract this number from the carbohydrate number to determine the net carbs. However, if the polyols are listed on a separate line and not indented, they have already been subtracted and the carbohydrate number provided is the net carbohydrates.

Allulose, a newer sweetener discussed in more detail in the next section, is an indigestible carbohydrate that can be fully deducted from the total carbohydrate value. At present, labelling protocol for products containing allulose is inconsistent. The carbohydrates allulose contributes to the total carbohydrate value may not appear on the nutritional label itself, in which case you may have to search the product packaging to find the applicable deduction.

Keto-friendly sweeteners

Traditional natural sweeteners such as sugars, syrups, fruit juices, and dates are carbohydrate-rich and typically avoided on a ketogenic diet. Luckily, several keto-friendly sweeteners are available, including stevia, monk fruit, erythritol, xylitol, and allulose, which come in standalone forms or in blends.

Stevia and monk fruit are highly concentrated carbohydrate and calorie-free sweeteners. In their pure liquid or powdered form, only a small amount is needed to achieve desired sweetness. Though sweet, stevia and monk fruit do not taste like sugar, and, on their own, are not a structural substitute for sugar in recipes.

Erythritol, xylitol, and allulose are bulkier sweeteners and come in various sugar-like and syrup forms. They may be blended with one of the aforementioned sweeteners to boost their sweetness to sugar-like levels, and are often touted as 1:1 substitutes for sugar.

Erythritol and xylitol are sugar alcohols, which are neither sugars nor alcohols, but structurally similar to both. While quite sugar-like, sugar alcohols have a slightly different taste profile to that of sugar and can create a cooling sensation in the mouth. Sugar alcohols can cause digestive upset in some, especially if consumed in large amounts. Pet owners should be aware that xylitol is toxic to dogs.

Allulose is not a sugar alcohol, has a taste profile very similar to that of sugar, and is unlikely to cause digestive upset, making it my sweetener of choice. It also retains moisture and caramelizes like sugar. Unfortunately, allulose is not currently available worldwide.

Allulose and erythritol are indigestible and are thus typically not included in net carb count. However, there is some debate when it comes to other sugar alcohols, which are caloric and digestible to varying degrees and at varying rates. This includes xylitol. If not avoiding these sugar alcohols entirely, some choose to only partially deduct the carbohydrates they contribute from the total carbohydrate value. Other sugar alcohols that can often be found in keto-friendly or diabetic products, and that may impact ketosis, are glycerin/glycerol, inositol, maltitol, and sorbitol. Of these, maltitol has the most potential to be problematic to maintaining ketosis.

Sweeteners need not be included in a ketogenic diet, and some choose to avoid both traditional and keto-friendly sweeteners altogether. Whether physiological or psychological, individual responses to the use of sweeteners may vary. Anecdotally, some have reported that including sweeteners in their diet has hindered their progress when it comes to reaching weight loss goals.

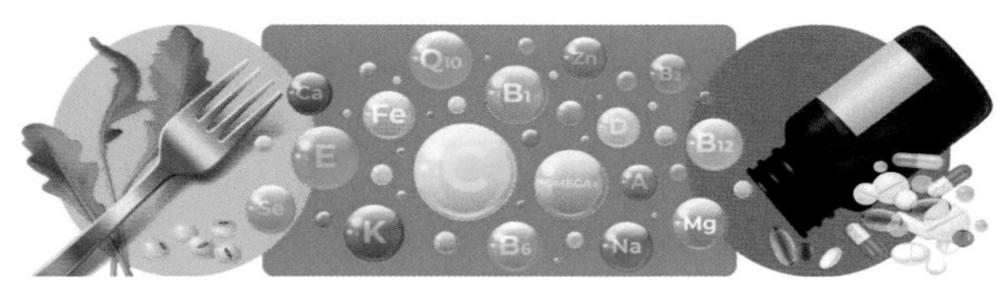

Micronutrients

Vitamins and minerals are essential nutrients that the body requires in small amounts for proper functioning and overall health. A well-planned and diverse vegan ketogenic diet rich in whole foods can meet most, but not all, nutritional needs. Supplementation and/or the use of fortified foods will be required to meet certain needs.

Attention should be paid to ensuring micronutrient needs are being met, and adjustments made to correct insufficiencies. The following list may be helpful in making dietary adjustments. Suggestions are tailored to a ketogenic diet, taking into account a food's net carb content. As a result, certain foods are not featured or highlighted.

B vitamins, with the exception of B12, are naturally present in a variety of plant foods. Additionally, some foods are commonly fortified with certain B vitamins, including B12. Plant milks and nutritional yeast are popular fortified foods that can easily be included in a vegan ketogenic diet. Without fortification, nutritional yeast remains a good source of B1, B2, B5, and B6, though amounts vary by brand and processing method. Check product labels for accurate B vitamin content of fortified foods and nutritional yeast.

- **Vitamin B1** (THIAMIN) is most prevalent in nuts and seeds, including chia seeds, flax seeds, hemp hearts, and sunflower seeds. Edamame and soybeans are also good sources.
- **Vitamin B2** (RIBOFLAVIN) content is high in almonds, edamame, mushrooms, soybeans, and spinach. Alfalfa sprouts, avocados, broccoli, and kale also contain reasonable amounts.
- **Vitamin B3** (NIACIN) is most notable in avocados, chia seeds, hemp hearts, mushrooms, peanuts, and sunflower seeds.
- **Vitamin B5** (PANTOTHENIC ACID) content is significant in avocados and mushrooms, and noteworthy in alfalfa sprouts and broccoli.
- **Vitamin B6** (PYRIDOXINE) is abundant in avocados, chia seeds, hemp hearts, kale, pistachios, soybeans, spinach, and sunflower seeds. It is also reasonably high in bok choy, broccoli, flax seeds, hazelnuts, sesame seeds, walnuts, and zucchini.
- **Vitamin B9** (FOLATE) content is substantial in most leafy greens, particularly kale, Romaine lettuce, and spinach. Avocados, beets, broccoli, edamame, and leafy green herbs also contain high amounts. Quantities in soybeans and sunflower seeds are notable.
- **Vitamin B12** (COBALAMIN) is generally not found in unfortified plant-based foods, apart from unpredictable and negligible amounts that may be present in seaweed and certain mushrooms. Consume foods fortified with B12 and/or supplement. Monitoring B12 levels via regular bloodwork is advisable.

Choline is present in a wide range of plant foods, although the levels are not particularly high. Above average amounts can be found in artichokes, edamame, certain mushrooms (enoki, maitake, and oyster), and soybeans. Broccoli, cauliflower, chia seeds, flax seeds, heart of palm, hemp hearts, other mushrooms, pumpkin seeds, and spinach provide lower but notable amounts.

Vitamin A, or more specifically provitamin A carotenoids, are abundant in dark green, orange, and red vegetables. Carrots, chard, kale, leaf lettuce, Romaine lettuce, and spinach are particularly rich sources. For use, the body converts provitamin A carotenoids into retinol, the bioavailable form of vitamin A. The conversion rate varies by type of carotenoid. Vitamin A intake should be measured in retinol activity equivalents (RAE) to account for the conversion of provitamin A carotenoids to retinol.

Vitamin C content is reasonably high in most vegetables, and particularly plentiful in bell peppers, broccoli, and kale. Quantities are also quite high in Brussels sprouts, cabbages (especially bok choy), chard, leafy green herbs, snow peas, and spinach. Low-sugar berries, lemons, and limes can also contribute to vitamin C intake.

Vitamin D is not naturally found in most foods. Mushrooms may contain small amounts, and some foods are fortified with vitamin D. However, vitamin D is derived mainly from sun exposure. Those with limited sun exposure, darker skin tone, or certain medical conditions may need to supplement to ensure adequate levels.

Vitamin E is not abundant in most plant foods. However, significant amounts exist in almonds, avocados, hazelnuts, olives, pine nuts, sunflower seeds, and oils derived from these items. Chard, cilantro, kale, radicchio, and spinach are noteworthy vegetable sources. Vitamin E also exists in soybean oil and some other vegetable oils.

Vitamin K content is high in most green vegetables, especially leafy greens like chard, kale, and spinach. It is also found in avocados, edamame, leafy green herbs, and soybeans. With the exception of chia seeds and pistachios, nuts and seeds contain little vitamin K.

Calcium is minimal in most plant foods, with some exceptions. Arugula, chia seeds, poppy seeds, and sesame seeds are calcium-rich. Almonds, bok choy, collards, kale, flax seeds, spinach, soybeans, and tahini also contain reasonable amounts. Plant-based milks are often fortified with calcium, and tofu is high in calcium due to the use of calcium sulfate as a coagulant.

Copper is abundant in alfalfa sprouts, avocados, chard, edamame, kale, leafy green herbs, nuts, olives, radicchio, seeds, and soybeans. Meeting your copper needs is unlikely to be a challenge.

Iron content is not high in most plant foods. Plant-based foods containing decent amounts include basil, chia seeds, edamame, flax seeds, hemp hearts, parsley, poppy seeds, pumpkin seeds, sesame seeds, soybeans, spinach, tahini, and tofu. Some plant-based milks and meats are fortified with iron. The iron in plant-based foods is non-heme iron, which the body absorbs less easily than heme iron. Rates of absorption vary by circumstance. Monitoring iron levels via regular bloodwork is advisable. Supplementation may be required.

Magnesium is most prevalent in nuts and seeds, with the exception of cashews, macadamia nuts, pecans, and pistachios. Arugula, basil, chard, edamame, soybeans, and spinach are also good sources.

Manganese is plentiful in most nuts and seeds, as well as in arugula, beets, blackberries, chard, coconut, collards, edamame, heart of palm, kale, peanuts, raspberries, soybeans, and spinach. Consuming adequate manganese is unlikely to present a challenge.

Phosphorus content is high in most nuts and seeds, especially chia seeds, flax seeds, hemp hearts, and pumpkin seeds, as well as in edamame, peanuts, and soybeans. Good amounts also exist in alfalfa sprouts, artichokes, celeriac, kale, and mushrooms.

Potassium, an electrolyte, is found in almost all plant foods, yet can be challenging to consume in sufficient quantities. Items especially high in potassium include avocados, cilantro, edamame, hemp hearts, kale, soybeans, and spinach. Arugula, broccoli, chard, flax seeds, and mushrooms have lower, but substantial, amounts.

Adequate intake of potassium can be of particular concern on a ketogenic diet due to certain inherent changes that take place within the body when carbohydrate intake is severely restricted. Insufficient potassium intake can lead to muscle cramps, fatigue, weakness, and heart palpitations, which are associated with electrolyte imbalance. Severe electrolyte imbalance can lead to serious health consequences. For those who are unable to meet their potassium needs through diet alone, supplementing with a carb-free potassium-rich electrolyte powder or a potassium salt (e.g. potassium chloride or potassium citrate) may be beneficial. However, be aware that excessive potassium supplementation, especially in concentrated doses, can also cause electrolyte imbalance and so is not without risk. Supplement responsibly.

Selenium content is negligible in most plant foods. However, a single Brazil nut will supply you with the daily recommended intake. Other notable sources of selenium are chia seeds, flax seeds, hemp hearts, mushrooms, sesame seeds, soybeans, and sunflower seeds.

Sodium content is minimal in unprocessed whole foods and most sodium in the diet comes from processed or packaged foods that contain added sodium, or when salt is added to dishes. In addition to salting your foods, good sources of sodium are salted nuts and seeds, kimchi, olives, pickles, sauerkraut, and vegetable broths.

Like potassium, sodium is an electrolyte and plays a crucial role in maintaining the body's electrolyte balance, and, like potassium, sufficient intake can be of particular concern due to certain inherent changes that occur when carbohydrate intake is severely restricted. On a carb-rich diet, sodium is typically retained. Conversely, on a ketogenic diet, sodium excretion is comparably high. Problems maintaining electrolyte balance may arise if sodium intake is limited or insufficient. If prescribed a low-sodium diet, discuss the implications of adopting a ketogenic diet with your physician.

Zinc content is particularly high in nuts and seeds, especially chia seeds, flax seeds, hemp hearts, pine nuts, poppy seeds, pumpkin seeds, and sesame seeds, and in alfalfa sprouts, basil, and soybeans.

Iodine is found mainly in seaweed, and can also be incorporate into the diet by using iodized salt. Iodine supplementation is an option for those unable to meet their needs via dietary sources alone.

Supplementation can be helpful in ensuring adequate vitamin and mineral intake and in preventing/addressing deficiencies. However, it is important to supplement sensibly. Excessive or unregulated supplementation can lead to imbalances or toxicity and should be discussed with a healthcare professional to ensure appropriate, safe, and effective dosage levels for your individual needs.

Vegan keto superfoods

Because of their nutrient profile, certain foods could be considered *super* in the context of a vegan ketogenic diet. I've divided what I deem to be vegan keto superfoods into three categories: primary superfoods, secondary superfoods, and super helpful foods.

Primary superfoods have a very low net carb content and so can be consumed in large quantities. In this category I've placed alfalfa sprouts, avocados, broccolini, chia seeds, flax seeds, hemp hearts, leafy green vegetables (especially spinach) and leafy green herbs, mushrooms, nutritional yeast, pumpkin seeds, soybeans, and tofu.

Secondary superfoods are somewhat higher in net carbs and so, depending on one's carb limit, quantities one can consume may be more limited. This category includes almonds, asparagus, broccoli, edamame, peanuts, sesame seeds, sunflower seeds, and tahini.

The super helpful foods category includes lupini beans, pea-based TVP, protein powder, and soy and pea milks (preferably fortified), all of which are great sources of protein. Also in this category are Brazil nuts (for selenium), cauliflower (as a substitute for rice or potatoes), nori (for iodine), olive oil (for healthy fats and vitamin E), and fermented foods (for gut-friendly probiotics).

Keto concerns

While research has shown potential benefits to adopting a ketogenic diet, especially for conditions related to overweight or obesity, neurological disorders, and inflammatory diseases, critics have valid concerns. The diet has been associated with an increased risk of developing nutrient deficiencies, cardiac disease, and cancer. Some argue that these risks could be mitigated with a nutritionally well-formulated and less animal-based approach. However, it needs to be acknowledged that there is currently insufficient evidence to suggest that a well-formulated vegan or plant-based ketogenic diet is entirely risk-free or healthful in the long term. Any concerns about adopting a vegan ketogenic diet should be discussed with a qualified healthcare professional. Now, let's explore some possible struggles you may encounter when adopting a ketogenic diet.

Keto flu is one of the most common short-term negative side effects of a ketogenic diet and is often experienced in the initial stages of adopting the diet, while the body is adapting. Keto flu typically involves headaches, brain fog, low energy levels, and an overall feeling of malaise. Feelings of thirst and dehydration may also be experienced. The severity and duration of keto flu varies among individuals. Increasing one's intake of fluids, salt/sodium, and of potassium and magnesium-rich foods may help minimize symptoms. Supplementing with the aforementioned minerals may also be helpful, but should be approached sensibly. Please read the information about potassium and sodium given on the previous page. Gradually easing into a ketogenic diet may also help lessen the severity of keto flu, although some argue that this may extend the overall adaptation period, and thus could be counterproductive.

Keto rash is relatively rare. The exact cause of keto rash, also known as prurigo pigmentosa or ketosis-associated dermatitis, is not fully understood, but may be related to the metabolic changes induced by a ketogenic diet. With any rash, maintaining good hygiene is essential. Keep the affected area clean and dry. If the rash persists, see a healthcare professional for an accurate diagnosis and treatment. Anecdotally, some individuals have reported that increasing their net carb intake, while still following a low-carb or ketogenic diet, has helped alleviate the rash. If you've developed a rash, keep in mind that it may not be keto related. Infections or allergies, including food allergies, may be the culprit.

Digestive complications can occur when making significant dietary changes, such as markedly increasing legume, fiber, or fat intake. Consumption of sugar alcohols, prebiotic fibers such as inulin, and certain obscure keto-friendly ingredients can cause bloating, gas, and digestive distress. Pay attention to how your body responds to unfamiliar foods/ingredients and adjust accordingly. Constipation may be related to inadequate sodium and potassium intake. Digestive complications may resolve over time as the body adapts, but some may find it beneficial to make dietary changes gradually.

Hair loss has been anecdotally reported as a side effect of a ketogenic diet. Hair loss can also be related to insufficient nutrition, including inadequate protein intake, severe calorie restriction, and sustained rapid weight loss. Ensure your nutritional needs are being fully met, and if restricting calories, take a moderate approach.

Insomnia can be a side effect of a ketogenic diet for some individuals. Insomnia can also result from severe calorie restriction as well as other factors unrelated to diet. Anecdotally, some have found relief by eating their most carbohydrate and/or calorie-heavy meal in the evening or by having a higher-carb snack before bed.

Exercise performance may suffer, in the short term, while the body adapts to the use of fat as its primary fuel source. Don't overexert yourself. Your performance should rebound over time and may even reach new heights once fully adapted.

Elevated LDL cholesterol levels are experienced by some who adopt a ketogenic diet, and may be cause for concern. Seek the advice of a healthcare professional on this matter. Limiting the consumption of saturated fat may serve to prevent an increase in, or reduce, LDL cholesterol levels in some individuals.

Conclusion

Adopting a vegan ketogenic diet can be both rewarding and challenging. However, armed with the basics and a mind open to culinary adventure, you are well on your way to vegan keto success!

General Book **notes**

The recipes

Flavors and spice: dishes tend to be bold in flavor. Garlic, ginger, herbs, and spices are used generously and chilis or crushed red pepper flakes appear often. Those who prefer milder flavors may wish to reduce the quantities of these ingredients to suit their palate.

Authenticity: dishes may not entirely embody the authentic flavors of the cuisines they represent. This is partially due to carbohydrate limitations, but also to avoid the use of uncommon ingredients and complex preparation methods. You will find terms such as *faux*, *-y*, *-ish*, *-esque*, and *-inspired* used liberally in the naming of recipes.

Carb-booster options: some recipes have options to raise their net carb content. These options are for those who prefer a diet higher in net carbs and/or a diet that includes a wider variety of foods. While some options are so-called keto-friendly foods, many are not considered compliant with a strict ketogenic diet. This is intentional and has been done with both nutrition and enjoyment in mind.

Eating larger amounts of low-carb foods is also a way to boost your net carb intake. This approach may be more suitable for those who enjoy substantial, bulky meals, or those who seek to meet a greater portion of their protein requirement via vegetable consumption.

Allergen-free options: when possible, substitutions are included in recipes containing common allergens like coconut, nuts, peanuts, and soy. All recipes are gluten-free unless a carb-booster option containing gluten is added. Allergen-free options aim to be both nutritionally and structurally similar to the original recipe. However, soy-free options using starchier beans are unavoidably higher in net carbs and lower in protein. Soybean-containing recipes have been strategically crafted to accommodate this bean swap while, usually, keeping the net carbs per serving under 15g, thus allowing the soy-free versions to be incorporated into a ketogenic diet.

To prevent clutter on the recipe page, macro details (Ⓜ) for options and variations are only provided when the difference from the original recipe exceeds 10%. A more comprehensive list of details can be found on page 98 or downloaded from keto4vegans.com.

Ingredients

The obscure: effort has been made to minimize the use of obscure and hard-to-find ingredients. However, some unique, but common to keto, ingredients have been included in the recipes. Whenever possible, alternatives to these items have been provided.

Soy and pea milk: many recipes include the use of soy or pea milk. The purpose of this is twofold, to increase the protein content of recipes as well as to take advantage of the vitamins and minerals these milks are typically fortified with. Occasionally, their use may add a structural component. Unsweetened milk should be used.

The recipes have been tested using soymilk. Most recipes have not been tested using pea milk or other plant milks. Depending on the nature of the recipe, results using these other milks may vary.

Onions: with the exception of green onion, most recipes do not specify which type of onion to use. Yellow, white, and red onions can be used interchangeably. I typically use yellow onions for cooking and red onions for raw dishes such as salads. Feel free to use whichever type of onion you prefer or is easily available to you.

Cucumbers: cucumbers are being used unpeeled unless stated otherwise. Peel them if you prefer; this will reduce the net carbs.

Mushrooms: unless specified otherwise, white button mushrooms are being used in the recipes. Feel free to use other mushrooms that you enjoy. However, be aware that the nutritional profiles of mushrooms vary and so changes will affect a recipe's macros.

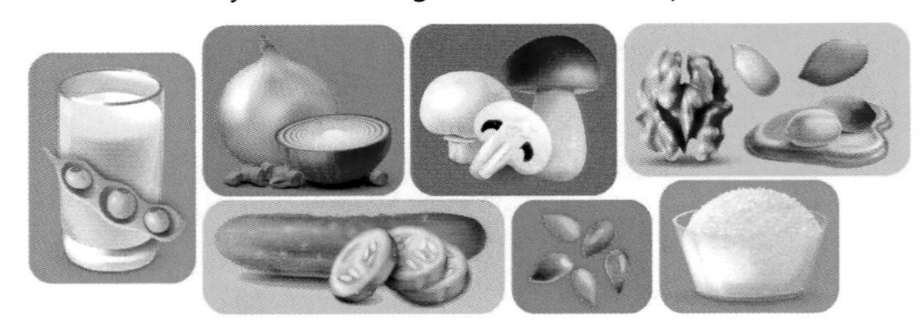

Flaxseed meal: I use golden flaxseed meal. It tends to have a lighter, less obtrusive flavor than brown flaxseed meal. Brown flax seeds can have quite an overpowering flavor that some may not enjoy.

Nuts, seeds, & their butters: apart from unhulled (i.e. brown or black) sesame seeds, measurements provided are for whole shelled nuts and seeds unless a specific cut is stated (e.g. slivered almonds). Feel free to buy pre-chopped items if applicable to the recipe and use the grams given to determine the required quantity.

Nutritional calculations are done with data for raw nuts and seeds unless the ingredient list specifies a particular roast (e.g. oil-roasted peanuts). Nuts and seeds that are toasted as part of the recipe are considered raw for macro calculations. If a recipe involves toasting a nut or seed, feel free to buy a toasted version and skip that step.

The nut/seed butters used in the recipes are unsweetened creamy types. However, using crunchy ones is unlikely to be problematic.

SWEETENERS: my preferred sweetener, allulose, is not available worldwide and thus most recipes have been tested with both allulose and erythritol. Recipes where allulose is minimal or where it does not serve a structural role have not been tested with an alternative sweetener (e.g. chia pudding and salad dressings).

PROTEIN POWDER: recipes that use plain pea protein powder have not been tested with other types of protein powder. Those with flavored protein powder have been made with Vega Sport Vanilla.

DIRECTIONS

Recipe directions do not typically include instructions to wash your vegetables or remove the inedible portions (peel, stems, seeds, pits, bad spots, etc.). Please assume that you are expected to wash and trim your produce appropriately before using it in the recipes.

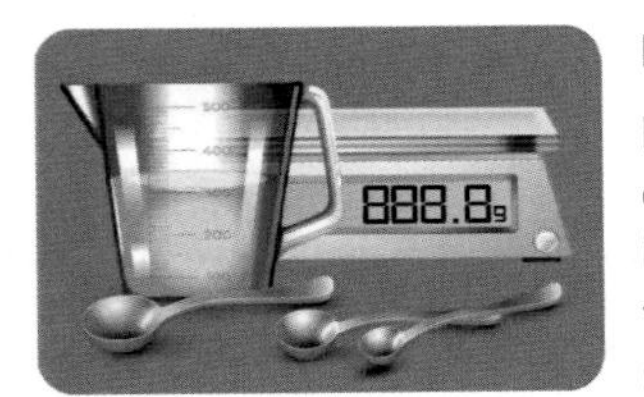

MEASUREMENTS

Effort has been made to ensure the content of this book is accessible to an international audience, as well as to those who do and do not use a kitchen scale. Typically, either gram or milliliter measurements are provided alongside cup and spoon quantities. For most wet/liquid ingredients, grams and milliliters are roughly equivalent. Grams and milliliters for amounts less than a tablespoon are not provided and so having a set of measuring spoons will be helpful. For those without measuring spoons, or who prefer to weigh their ingredients, a helpful chart can be found on page 100.

MACRO CALCULATIONS

For the most part, recipe macro calculations have been made using the NCCDB data provided in Cronometer. For certain items, data is not available and so product data has been used. You can find a list of products I use or suggest at keto4vegans.com. For a select few items, I have chosen not to use NCCDB data despite its availability. This is either because the data does not appear to be consistent with numerous products on the market, or because there is a high degree of variation brand to brand. The items I use brand-specific data for are chia seeds, hemp hearts, pumpkins seeds, sunflower seed butter, canned coconut milk, canned chopped tomatoes, bouillon cubes, brined lupini beans, tofu, and agar agar.

For accuracy, you may wish to recalculate recipe macros with the products you use. Keep in mind that there are pros and cons to using label data over more comprehensive national data. You can read more about tracking macros on page 7.

STORAGE

Always store leftover foods in sealed airtight containers. Be sure to completely cool baked goods, especially crunchy bars and crackers, prior to storage. Other items should at least be mostly cooled to prevent excessive moisture or steam build up inside containers.

DISCLAIMER

This book does not aim to promote ketogenic diets, veganism, calorie restriction, or any mix thereof. It intends to serve as a tool for those who have already made an informed decision to adopt a vegan ketogenic diet and who now seek to approach the diet in a healthful and sustainable manner. I, the author, do not possess any qualifications in medicine, dietetics, or nutrition, nor am I involved in research in any of these fields. Conscious effort has been made to avoid including information that would require the citation of scientific literature, which I am not qualified to interpret. Effort has also been made to avoid taking a position on topics that could be considered controversial, insubstantially supported by scientific literature, or contradictory to the large body of research that informs mainstream dietary guidelines and medical advice. I acknowledge that my decision to omit such content may frustrate those looking for answers about certain contentious health topics.

There are potential health consequences, both physical and mental, to engaging in dieting, and especially in diets that restrict the consumption of major food groups. It is advisable to discuss significant dietary changes, especially those intended to support medical conditions, with qualified and well-informed medical professionals. Please make your health decisions responsibly.

SUPPORT & RESOURCES

Visit the website, keto4vegans.com, to download printable book content and access other resources. For support with recipes or other book-related inquiries you can email me at keto4vegans@gmail.com and/or join the Keto4Vegans Facebook community where you can interact with both myself and other book owners. Make sure to answer all of the questions and read and agree to the group rules in order to gain access. To engage with the wider vegan keto community, I'd suggest joining the well-established Facebook group Vegan Keto Made Simple.

VEGAN KETO **food list**

The structure of this food list enables the user to determine not only *what* can be included in a vegan ketogenic diet, but also *how much* of each item can be consumed. Note that the consumption guidance is slanted towards individuals with a carb limit at the lower end of the ketogenic range (i.e. 20 to 30g net carbs). Those with a higher carb limit may be able to consume items more generously than advised by the section headings. A printable copy of this food list, and variations of it, can be found at keto4vegans.com/resources.

⚠C higher net carbs than other items in the section ♥ good protein source 💧 good fat source ✎ see notes (page 17)
👀 check your labels (net carbs are often higher↑ or lower↓ than national data suggests) ⚠V often non-vegan (check ingredients)

vegetables & mushrooms

EAT IN abundance

- alfalfa sprouts ♥
- arugula ♥
- asparagus ♥
- bamboo shoots, canned
- basil ♥
- beet greens ♥
- Belgian endive
- bok choy ♥
- broccolini ♥
- broccoli raab ♥
- celery
- chard
- chives ♥
- cilantro ♥
- collard greens ♥
- cucumber
- escarole ♥
- frisée ♥
- grape leaves, canned ♥ 👀
- heart of palm, canned
- kale ♥ ✎
- lettuce
- mushrooms: morel, portabella, straw (canned), and white ♥
- mustard greens ♥
- napa cabbage
- radishes
- spinach ♥
- summer squash
- watercress ♥
- zucchini

EAT IN moderation

- artichoke hearts, marinated in oil 👀↓
- banana blossoms, in brine 👀
- bean sprouts (mung bean)
- broccoflower
- broccoli, incl. Tenderstem ♥
- cabbage, green and savoy
- cauliflower
- calabash gourd
- chayote
- eggplant
- fennel
- green beans
- green bell pepper
- green onions
- jackfruit, young green, canned in brine 👀
- jalapeño peppers
- jicama
- kale ✎
- kohlrabi
- mushrooms: cremini, enoki, maitake, oyster, and shiitake
- okra
- parsley
- radicchio
- red bell pepper
- rhubarb
- snow peas
- tomatoes, incl. canned ✎
- turnips
- turnip greens
- wax beans

EAT sparingly

- artichoke hearts, cooked and canned 👀↓
- beets
- Brussels sprouts
- cabbage, red
- carrots
- celeriac
- chili peppers, green or red
- fava beans, cooked from fresh
- garlic ⚠C
- ginger root ⚠C
- onions
- peas, green, canned 👀 ✎
- pumpkin
- rutabaga
- spaghetti squash
- yellow bell pepper

LIMIT

- acorn and butternut squash
- corn, canned ⚠C 👀 ✎
- leeks ⚠C
- peas, green, fresh and frozen 👀 ✎
- tomatoes, sun-dried, in oil ⚠C 👀

AVOID

- corn, fresh, frozen, and popped ⚠C
- Jerusalem artichoke
- parsnips
- potatoes, white and sweet
- shallots
- yams

fruit (including avocados)

EAT IN abundance

- açai, unsweetened
- avocados

EAT IN moderation

- blackberries
- huckleberries
- starfruit

EAT sparingly

- cantaloupe
- grapefruit, white
- lemons, incl. juice
- limes, incl. juice
- peaches
- pear, Asian
- raspberries
- strawberries
- watermelon

LIMIT

- apples
- apricots
- blueberries
- cherries
- cranberries
- currants
- dragon fruit
- grapefruit, pink and red
- guava
- honeydew melon
- kiwis, green
- nectarines
- oranges
- papaya
- pears
- pineapple
- plums

AVOID

- bananas
- dried fruit, esp. dates
- figs
- fruit juice
- grapes
- jackfruit, ripe
- kiwis, sungold
- lychees
- mango
- passionfruit
- plantain
- pomegranate

nuts & seeds (including coconut & peanuts)

For the most part, items in this category are good sources of both protein and fat. However, coconut, macadamia nuts, and pine nuts are not particularly high in protein, and cashews and pistachios have a low protein content relative to their net carb content.

EAT IN abundance

- Brazil nuts
- chia seeds
- flax seeds
- hemp hearts
- pecans
- pilinuts
- pumpkin seeds
- sacha inchi seeds
- sesame seeds, hulled (i.e. white)
- sunflower seed butter

EAT IN moderation

- almonds
- coconut
- hazelnuts
- macadamia nuts
- peanuts, oil-roasted
- pine nuts
- poppy seeds
- walnuts

EAT sparingly

- peanuts, dry-roasted
- peanut butter
- sesame seeds, unhulled (i.e. brown and black)
- sunflower seeds
- tahini

LIMIT

- pistachios

AVOID

- acorns
- cashews
- chestnuts, roasted

legumes & other protein-rich foods

Many items in this category will have nutritional profiles that are brand specific, vary widely by brand, and differ substantially from national nutritional data. Therefore, it is prudent to check your labels. Consumption suggestions are based on the use of lower-carb items.

Eat in abundance

- hemp seed tofu
- lupin, ground/flakes
- lupini beans, some brands (e.g. Brami & Unico)
- nori, dried
- nutritional yeast flakes
- pea milk, unsweetened
- plant-based meats with 1-2g net carbs per 10g protein
- pumpkin seed tofu (pumfu)
- protein powder, very low-carb varieties
- soybeans, cooked from dried
- soy yogurt, unsweetened
- textured vegetable protein (TVP), pea-based
- tofu, especially extra and super firm varieties
- tortilla chips, pea protein-based (e.g. BeyondChipz)
- yuba/fresh bean curd sheets

Eat in moderation

- edamame, incl. dry-roasted
- Just® Egg, scramble
- plant-based meats with 1-2g net carbs per 5g protein
- seitan, lower-carb recipes
- soybeans, dry or oil-roasted
- soybean or edamame pastas
- soymilk, unsweetened
- tempeh
- textured soy protein (TSP)
- textured vegetable protein (TVP), soy-based
- wraps/tortillas, certain low-carb high-protein varieties (e.g. Mission Hill & BFree)

Plant-based "dairy"

Plant-based dairy alternatives tend to be low in protein and high in starch, and thus high in net carbs. Some low-carb options do exist. If an item is not low-carb, enjoy it sparingly.

Eat sparingly

- lupini beans, some brands (e.g. Cento)
- plant-based meats with 1-2g net carbs per 3g protein
- soybeans, canned/jarred (e.g. Eden & Biona)
- soy wrappers/norigami

Limit

- beans (apart from soy and lupini)
- lentils
- plant-based meats with net carbs equal to protein
- split peas

Avoid

- grains and pseudograins: amaranth, barley, buckwheat, bulgar, couscous, kamut, kaniwa, millet, oats, quinoa, rice (incl. wild), rye, semolina, sorghum, spelt, teff, and wheat
- plant-based meats with more net carbs than protein

baking ingredients

Flours & meals

With the exception of coconut flour and oat fiber powder, items in this section are good sources of protein.

- almond flour
- coconut flour
- flaxseed meal
- lupin flour
- oat fiber powder
- peanut flour/peanut butter powder
- protein powder, plain and flavored
- sacha inchi powder
- sesame seed flour
- soybean flour
- vital wheat gluten

Miscellaneous

- agar agar
- aquafaba (i.e. chickpea water)
- baking chocolate, unsweetened
- baking powder
- baking soda
- cacao nibs
- chocolate chips, dark, keto-friendly varieties
- cocoa/cacao powder, unsweetened
- coconut milk and cream, canned
- cream of tartar
- extracts/flavors, sugar-free
- gums (guar, xanthan, etc.)
- herbs & spices
- oils and butters, all types
- pumpkin purée, canned, unsweetened
- psyllium husks, whole and powdered
- yeast, dry active

Sweeteners

- allulose
- Bocha Sweet
- erythritol
- monk fruit
- stevia
- xylitol

Limit

- apple sauce, unsweetened
- chickpea flour
- starches/starch-like flours: arrowroot, cassava, corn, potato, and tapioca

Avoid

- carob
- cornmeal/corn flour
- dried fruit, esp. dates
- grain and pseudograin flours
- sugars and syrups, traditional natural types

other items

Items in this category often contain added sugar and can be quite high in net carbs. For some items, it's not uncommon for the net carbs to be significantly higher than national nutritional data suggests. Check your labels and choose your products wisely. Avoid high-sugar items and use items that contain lesser amounts of sugar sparingly.

Pickled & fermented foods

capers
ginger, artificially sweetened
jalapeños, jarred/canned in brine
kimchi
olives
pickles, cucumber, dill
sauerkraut

Miscellaneous

algae powders, e.g. chlorella and spirulina
chocolate, very dark varieties (e.g. Lindt 90%)
kelp noodles
MCT oil powder
seaweed, certain varieties
shirataki/konjac noodles and rice

Cooking complements

bouillon cubes/powder and vegetable broth
coconut milk and cream
curry pastes
herbs & spices
liquid smoke
marinara and tomato-based pasta sauces
miso paste
oils, all types
pesto
sambal oelek
tomato paste
Worcestershire sauce

Condiments

aminos, incl. coconut
buttery spreads
hot sauce
ketchup
mayonnaise
mustard
salsa, jarred, tomato-based
tamari/soy sauce
vinegars, most types (excl. balsamic)
wasabi paste

Beverages

coffee, black
diet sodas and soda water
milks, plant-based (excl. oat and cashew)
tea, black and herbal

See note about alcohol consumption.

Notes & Tips

***Kale** underwent a nutritional transformation (5.0g → 0.2g net carbs per 100g) in 2019 when the USDA made changes to its database.*

***Canned** and **frozen vegetables** often contain added sugar. Corn, green peas, and tomatoes are frequent targets. Check your labels.*

***Chia seed, hemp heart, pumpkin seed**, and **sunflower seed butter** consumption recommendations are based on label data, which is consistently much lower in net carbs than national data.*

***Lupini beans** and lupin derivatives may cause digestive distress to those not well-adapted to frequent bean consumption.*

There is a link between peanut allergies and lupin allergies. Thus, approach lupini beans with caution if you have a peanut allergy.

The nutritional data on lupini beans varies vastly by brand. Reasons for this are unclear. Check your labels.

***Nutritional yeast flakes** come in fortified and unfortified varieties. You may wish you blend these varieties to avoid excessive intake of the micronutrients that nutritional yeast is commonly fortified with.*

The net carb content of nutritional yeast can vary substantially, likely due in part to the substrate used for growing it. Check your labels.

***Tofu** net carb and protein content varies a lot by type. Firmer and non-silken varieties tend to be lower in carbs and higher in protein, while softer and silken varieties tend to be higher in carbs and lower in protein. However, this is not always the case, so check your labels.*

***Tempeh** can sometimes be very low in net carbs, and if so, can be eaten in abundance. Lightlife makes some very low-carb options.*

***MCT oil** can cause nausea or stomach aches in some people, especially if consumed in large amounts and/or on an empty stomach.*

*The health consequences of aspartame consumption, a common sweetener in **diet sodas**, has recently come under scrutiny. However, at the time of writing, these new insights have not necessitated or led to a change in previously established intake guidelines.*

***Alcohol** is not entirely off limits on a keto diet. Pure alcohols such as rum, vodka, gin, tequila, and whiskey contain no carbs. Dry wines and light beers are not overly carb heavy (about 4g net carbs for a 5-ounce [150ml] glass of wine and 2.5 to 6g for a 12-ounce [350ml] beer). Be aware that some people report a much lower alcohol tolerance when in ketosis, especially in the initial stages.*

***Gums** and **psyllium husks** may cause digestive upset or urgency in some people, especially if consumed in large quantities.*

***Xylitol** is toxic to dogs. Pet owners should exercise caution.*

TOSSED SALAD **builder**

A tossed green salad is a healthy and refreshing mix of leafy greens combined with an assortment of raw vegetables, occasional fruits, and additional crunchy ingredients such as nuts, seeds, or croutons. These items are topped with a dressing and tossed together in a bowl to ensure an even distribution of flavors and textures. The purpose of this tool is to enable you to build a low-carb version of such a salad.

Salad items are grouped by net carb content and divided into three categories: **vegetables** and **fruit**, **nuts and seeds**, and dressings and **dressing components**. Leafy green options are listed separately. To the right of each item are values associated with the item's calories, protein, fat, and net carb content. These values are based on the item's gram quantity, unless one is not provided. Once an item has been selected for your salad, either note down these values on a sheet of paper, or mark them on a copy of the builder itself. A printable version can be downloaded from keto4vegans.com/resources. Feel free to double, triple, or halve given portions of items and adjust the values accordingly. When selecting quantities of dressings or dressing components, keep in mind how much you'll need to dress a salad having the amount of leafy greens you've selected. Once all items have been chosen, add up the values, insert them into the simple mathematical equations at the bottom right, and calculate the nutritional value of your salad.

Due to space constraints, tablespoons and teaspoons are abbreviated as Tbsp and tsp, respectively, and inches is abbreviated as "in". For reference, $1^1/_2$ tsp = $^1/_2$ Tbsp.

A TYPICAL house salad

Romaine, radish, tomato, cucumber (with peel), onion, sunflower seeds, and carrot, in quantities as per the builder, with 2 tablespoons (30ml) Garlic Oregano Vinaigrette.

Ⓜ 260 CALS | 4.0 PRO | 19 FAT | 7.0 NC

NOTES & TIPS ✎

Gram measurements are exact, while food-based measurements are gram-based approximations (i.e. 29g is roughly $^1/_4$ medium tomato).

Values in this tool are rounded for ease of use. The approximate nutritional value of a salad constructed with this tool will typically be within ±10% of its true value.

Most data used in creating this tool comes from US nutritional databases. However, data for a select few items is brand specific.

Some of the "NET CARB FREEBIES" are not entirely carb-free. Net carbs will accumulate if using large quantities of items marked with an asterisk (*).

Check your labels 👀 for condiments, sauces, and other marked items, which can often be higher ↑ (or lower ↓) in net carbs than expected.

Items with yellow boxes, or marked with a yellow droplet ●, are food sources of fat. Nuts, seeds, and their butters are also good sources of protein. However, the amounts of these items listed here are quite small. For some more substantial protein options, see the "PROTEIN-RICH toppings or sides" section on page 37.

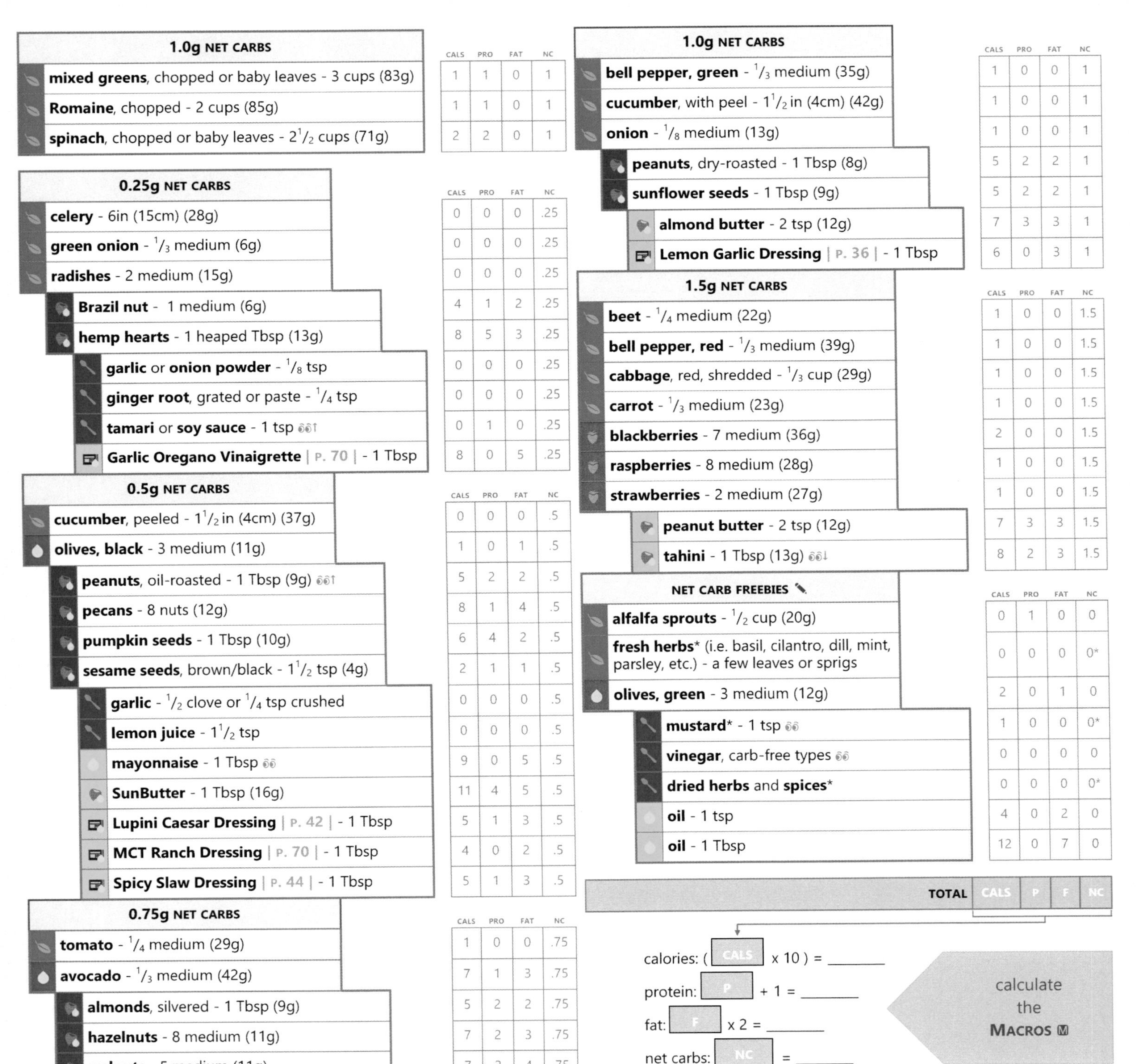

1.0g NET CARBS	CALS	PRO	FAT	NC
mixed greens, chopped or baby leaves - 3 cups (83g)	1	1	0	1
Romaine, chopped - 2 cups (85g)	1	1	0	1
spinach, chopped or baby leaves - $2^1/_2$ cups (71g)	2	2	0	1

0.25g NET CARBS	CALS	PRO	FAT	NC
celery - 6in (15cm) (28g)	0	0	0	.25
green onion - $^1/_3$ medium (6g)	0	0	0	.25
radishes - 2 medium (15g)	0	0	0	.25
Brazil nut - 1 medium (6g)	4	1	2	.25
hemp hearts - 1 heaped Tbsp (13g)	8	5	3	.25
garlic or **onion powder** - $^1/_8$ tsp	0	0	0	.25
ginger root, grated or paste - $^1/_4$ tsp	0	0	0	.25
tamari or **soy sauce** - 1 tsp	0	1	0	.25
Garlic Oregano Vinaigrette | P. 70 | - 1 Tbsp	8	0	5	.25

0.5g NET CARBS	CALS	PRO	FAT	NC
cucumber, peeled - $1^1/_2$ in (4cm) (37g)	0	0	0	.5
olives, black - 3 medium (11g)	1	0	1	.5
peanuts, oil-roasted - 1 Tbsp (9g)	5	2	2	.5
pecans - 8 nuts (12g)	8	1	4	.5
pumpkin seeds - 1 Tbsp (10g)	6	4	2	.5
sesame seeds, brown/black - $1^1/_2$ tsp (4g)	2	1	1	.5
garlic - $^1/_2$ clove or $^1/_4$ tsp crushed	0	0	0	.5
lemon juice - $1^1/_2$ tsp	0	0	0	.5
mayonnaise - 1 Tbsp	9	0	5	.5
SunButter - 1 Tbsp (16g)	11	4	5	.5
Lupini Caesar Dressing | P. 42 | - 1 Tbsp	5	1	3	.5
MCT Ranch Dressing | P. 70 | - 1 Tbsp	4	0	2	.5
Spicy Slaw Dressing | P. 44 | - 1 Tbsp	5	1	3	.5

0.75g NET CARBS	CALS	PRO	FAT	NC
tomato - $^1/_4$ medium (29g)	1	0	0	.75
avocado - $^1/_3$ medium (42g)	7	1	3	.75
almonds, silvered - 1 Tbsp (9g)	5	2	2	.75
hazelnuts - 8 medium (11g)	7	2	3	.75
walnuts - 5 medium (11g)	7	2	4	.75

1.0g NET CARBS	CALS	PRO	FAT	NC
bell pepper, green - $^1/_3$ medium (35g)	1	0	0	1
cucumber, with peel - $1^1/_2$ in (4cm) (42g)	1	0	0	1
onion - $^1/_8$ medium (13g)	1	0	0	1
peanuts, dry-roasted - 1 Tbsp (8g)	5	2	2	1
sunflower seeds - 1 Tbsp (9g)	5	2	2	1
almond butter - 2 tsp (12g)	7	3	3	1
Lemon Garlic Dressing | P. 36 | - 1 Tbsp	6	0	3	1

1.5g NET CARBS	CALS	PRO	FAT	NC
beet - $^1/_4$ medium (22g)	1	0	0	1.5
bell pepper, red - $^1/_3$ medium (39g)	1	0	0	1.5
cabbage, red, shredded - $^1/_3$ cup (29g)	1	0	0	1.5
carrot - $^1/_3$ medium (23g)	1	0	0	1.5
blackberries - 7 medium (36g)	2	0	0	1.5
raspberries - 8 medium (28g)	1	0	0	1.5
strawberries - 2 medium (27g)	1	0	0	1.5
peanut butter - 2 tsp (12g)	7	3	3	1.5
tahini - 1 Tbsp (13g)	8	2	3	1.5

NET CARB FREEBIES	CALS	PRO	FAT	NC
alfalfa sprouts - $^1/_2$ cup (20g)	0	1	0	0
fresh herbs* (i.e. basil, cilantro, dill, mint, parsley, etc.) - a few leaves or sprigs	0	0	0	0*
olives, green - 3 medium (12g)	2	0	1	0
mustard* - 1 tsp	1	0	0	0*
vinegar, carb-free types	0	0	0	0
dried herbs and **spices***	0	0	0	0*
oil - 1 tsp	4	0	2	0
oil - 1 Tbsp	12	0	7	0
TOTAL	CALS	P	F	NC

calories: (CALS x 10) = ________

protein: P + 1 = ________

fat: F x 2 = ________

net carbs: NC = ________

calculate the **MACROS** M

VANILLA COCONUT CHIA **pudding**

YIELD 4 servings of roughly 1 cup (198g) each, totalling 4 cups (791g)

MACROS Ⓜ (per serving) 270 calories | 11g protein | 17g fat | 2.1g net carbs

PREP 15 minutes | **SET** preferably overnight, but a minimum of 1 hour

EQUIPMENT REQUIRED four 8-ounce (240ml) jars or airtight containers of choice

STORE refrigerated for up to 5 days.

Ingredients

1¾ cups (420ml) **soy** or **pea milk**

½ 13.5-ounce (200ml) can full-fat **coconut milk** or low-carb plant-based cooking cream

¼ cup (50g) granulated **allulose** or equivalent in keto-friendly sweetener of choice

1½ teaspoons **vanilla extract**

⅛ teaspoon **salt**

⅔ cup (107g) **chia seeds**

Fruit toppings

- açai, purée - 100g Ⓜ 61 CALS | 4.7 FAT | 1.2 NC
- apricot - 1 medium (35g) Ⓜ 3.1 NC
- blackberries - ¼ cup (36g) Ⓜ 1.5 NC
- cantaloupe - ¼ cup chopped (40g) Ⓜ 2.8 NC
- nectarine - ¼ medium (36g) Ⓜ 2.9 NC
- peach - ¼ medium (38g) Ⓜ 2.9 NC
- raspberries - ¼ cup (31g) Ⓜ 1.7 NC
- starfruit - ½ medium (46g) Ⓜ 1.8 NC
- strawberries - 4 medium (48g) Ⓜ 2.6 NC

Carb Booster (fruit) toppings

Use a greater quantity of the above fruits, or indulge in one these higher-carb options:

- apple - ¼ medium (46g) Ⓜ 4.8 NC
- banana - ¼ medium (30g) Ⓜ 6.0 NC
- blueberries - ¼ cup (37g) Ⓜ 4.5 NC
- cherries, sweet - 5 medium (41g) Ⓜ 4.8 NC
- kiwi, green - ½ medium (35g) Ⓜ 4.0 NC
- mango - ¼ cup chopped (48g) Ⓜ 6.3 NC
- passion fruit - 2 medium (36g) Ⓜ 4.7 NC
- pineapple - ¼ cup chopped (41g) Ⓜ 4.8 NC

Notes & Tips ✎

Excessive chia seed consumption can cause digestive distress. I'd suggest a 2-serving limit of this pudding.

Directions

-1- Put all ingredients, apart from the chia seeds, in a medium-sized mixing bowl.

-2- Add the chia seeds and whisk for 2 to 3 minutes. Continue to whisk occasionally for an additional 3 to 5 minutes to prevent clumping.

-3- Using a ladle, divide the pudding evenly between four 8-ounce (240ml) jars, or containers of choice. Seal and refrigerate for a minimum of one hour, but preferably overnight.

-4- Enjoy cold. See some topping options below.

Nut & Seed toppings

- almonds, slivered - ¼ cup (33g) Ⓜ 192 CALS | 7.0 PRO | 17 FAT | 2.8 NC
- Brazil nuts - 4 medium (19g) Ⓜ 125 CALS | 2.7 PRO | 13 FAT | 0.8 NC
- coconut, dried, shredded - ¼ cup (20g) Ⓜ 132 CALS | 1.4 PRO | 13 FAT | 1.5 NC
- hazelnuts - ¼ cup (34g) Ⓜ 212 CALS | 5.0 PRO | 21 FAT | 2.3 NC
- hemp hearts - 2 tablespoons (20g) Ⓜ 111 CALS | 6.3 PRO | 9.8 FAT | 0.9 NC
- macadamia nuts - ¼ cup (36g) Ⓜ 258 CALS | 2.8 PRO | 27 FAT | 1.9 NC
- peanuts, dry-roasted - ¼ cup (37g) Ⓜ 214 CALS | 8.9 PRO | 18 FAT | 4.6 NC
- pecans - ¼ cup (29g) Ⓜ 200 CALS | 2.7 PRO | 21 FAT | 1.2 NC
- pumpkin seeds - 2 tablespoons (20g) Ⓜ 118 CALS | 7.2 PRO | 8.9 FAT | 1.0 NC
- sesame seeds, brown or black - 2 tablespoons (18g) Ⓜ 103 CALS | 3.2 PRO | 8.9 FAT | 2.1 NC
- sunflower seeds - 2 tablespoons (18g) Ⓜ 105 CALS | 3.7 PRO | 9.2 FAT | 2.0 NC
- walnuts - ¼ cup (25g) Ⓜ 163 CALS | 3.8 PRO | 16 FAT | 1.7 NC

Recipe Variations

Chocolate Chia Pudding: increase the milk to 2 cups (480ml) and the sweetener to ½ cup (100g). Add ¼ cup + 2 tablespoons (32g) cocoa/cacao powder. Ⓜ (234g) 299 CALS | 13 PRO | 3.9 NC

Golden Milk Chia Pudding: add 1 tablespoon (18g) grated fresh ginger and 1½ teaspoons each of ground turmeric and ground cinnamon. Ⓜ (204g) 3.6 NC

Pumpkin Spice Chia Pudding: add ½ cup (123g) canned pumpkin purée and 1 teaspoon pumpkin spice. (229g) Ⓜ 3.9 NC

Toffee Latté Chia Pudding: add 1½ tablespoons (6g) instant coffee granules and 20 to 30 drops of toffee-flavored liquid stevia. Ⓜ (199g) 3.0 NC

Note: macro notes for recipe variations are per serving and are only provided when and where the difference from the original recipe macros exceeds 10%. Calories for most fruit toppings are minimal (about 15 to 35 calories); fat and protein are negligible. Topping macros do not include Chia Pudding.

CARROT CAKE BREAKFAST **bars**

YIELD 6 servings of 1 bar each, totalling 6 bars

MACROS Ⓜ (per serving) 236 calories | 11g protein | 19g fat | 3.6g net carbs

PREP 30 minutes | **BAKE** 20 to 23 minutes | **COOL** 15 minutes

EQUIPMENT REQUIRED a 7-inch (18cm) square baking pan or a 9 by 5-inch (23 by 13cm) loaf pan

STORE at room temperature for up to 24 hours or refrigerated for up to 5 days.

Wet Ingredients

2 tablespoons (30ml) room temperature **water**

1 tablespoon (8g) **flaxseed meal**

1 teaspoon **vanilla extract**

1/4 cup (63g) **almond butter**

1/4 cup (61g) canned **pumpkin purée**

1 1/2 tablespoons (23ml) melted **coconut oil** or neutral-flavored oil of choice

1/2 cup (64g) grated **carrot** (about 1 medium)

Dry Ingredients

1/2 cup (50g) **walnuts**, coarsely chopped

1/4 cup (40g) **hemp hearts**

1/3 cup (37g) vegan vanilla **protein powder**

3 tablespoons (38g) granulated **allulose** or granulated keto-friendly sweetener of choice

1 1/2 teaspoons **nutritional yeast flakes**

1 1/2 teaspoons ground **cinnamon**

1/2 teaspoon **baking powder**

1/8 teaspoon ground **nutmeg**

1/8 teaspoon **salt**

Allergen-Free Options

nut-free: replace the almond butter with sunflower seed butter and the walnuts with 1/3 cup (47g) sunflower seeds.

Carb Booster Options

Increase the water to 1/3 cup (80ml) and add 1/4 cup (28g) rolled oats alongside the flaxseed meal. Reduce the almond butter to 3 tablespoons (47g).
Ⓜ 6.0 NC

Note: macro notes are per serving and are only provided when and where the difference from the original recipe macros exceeds 10%.

Directions

-1- In a medium-sized mixing bowl, whisk together the water, flaxseed meal, and vanilla extract. Set aside to gel.

-2- Preheat the oven to 350°F (175°C).

-3- Prepare the carrot and walnuts as per the ingredient list.

-4- In a small mixing bowl, whisk together the dry ingredients.

-5- Line a 7-inch (18cm) square cake pan, or 9 by 5-inch (23 by 13cm) loaf pan, with parchment paper. Allow the parchment to hang over two sides for easy removal of the bars.

-6- Whisk the almond butter, pumpkin purée, and oil to the flax mixture.

-7- Add the carrot and the dry mixture to the wet mixture. Using a silicone spatula or mixing spoon, mix until a soft dough has formed and no dry patches remain.

-8- Transfer the dough to the lined pan. Using oiled hands or a clean silicone spatula, gently press the dough into an even layer.

-9- Place the pan in the center of the oven and bake for 20 to 23 minutes, or until the edges are dark golden brown.

-10- Remove the bars from the oven and allow them to cool in the pan for 5 minutes. Then, gently transfer the bars from the pan to a wire cooling rack to cool for an additional 10 minutes.

-11- Cut into 6 bars. Enjoy warm or at room temperature.

Recipe Variations

Fudgy Zucchini Breakfast Bars: replace the carrot with 1/2 cup (83g) grated zucchini (about 1/2 medium). Reduce the protein powder to 1/4 cup (28g) and add 1/4 cup (22g) unsweetened cocoa/cacao powder to the dry ingredients. Increase the allulose to 1/4 cup (50g). Omit the cinnamon and nutmeg.

Falafel-Inspired Breakfast Bars: see page 80 for the recipe.

Notes & Tips ✎

Add some extra crunch and depth of flavor to the walnuts by toasting them at 350°F (175°C) for 7 to 9 minutes before using them in this recipe. If using sunflower seeds, toast these for 5 to 7 minutes.

If doubling the recipe, use a 9-inch (23cm) square baking pan.

A loose bottom cake pan is a great tool to have for this recipe. MasterClass has a great selection of loose-bottom pans.

CRUNCHY GRANOLA **bars** or SOFT GRANOLA **cookies**

YIELD 20 servings of either 2 cookies or 1 bar each, totalling 40 cookies or 20 bars

MACROS Ⓜ (per serving) 272 calories
11g protein | 23g fat | 2.5g net carbs

PREP 35 minutes | **BAKE** 10 to 12 minutes for cookies; roughly 5 hours for bars | **COOL** 10 minutes

EQUIPMENT REQUIRED 2 medium-sized baking sheets

STORE cookies at room temperature for up to 48 hours or refrigerated for up to 5 days. Store bars, completely dehydrated and fully cooled, at room temperature for up to a month.

ALLERGEN-FREE OPTIONS

nut-free: omit the almond extract, walnuts, and Brazil nuts. Increase the pumpkin seeds to $^{3}/_{4}$ cup (120g) and add $^{3}/_{4}$ cup (105g) sunflower seeds. Replace the almond butter with sunflower seed butter.

CARB BOOSTER OPTIONS

Reduce the hemp hearts to $^{1}/_{2}$ cup (80g) and add $1^{1}/_{2}$ cups (165g) rolled oats to the dry ingredients. Ⓜ 7.2 NC

Replace the walnuts with 1 cup cashews (130g) or 1 cup (123g) pistachios. Ⓜ 3.9 NC or Ⓜ 3.2 NC

Note: macro notes are per serving and are only provided when and where the difference from the original recipe macros exceeds 10%.

Wet Ingredients

$^3/_4$ cup (180ml) **water**

$^1/_4$ cup (30g) **flaxseed meal**

2 teaspoons **almond extract**

2 teaspoons **vanilla extract**

$^1/_2$ cup (120ml/109g) melted **coconut oil** or neutral-flavored oil of choice

$^1/_2$ cup (125g) **almond butter**

Dry Ingredients

1 cup (100g) **walnuts**, chopped small

1 cup (160g) **hemp hearts**

$^1/_2$ cup (80g) **pumpkin seeds**

$^1/_4$ cup (39g) **Brazil nuts**, chopped small (about 8 nuts)

$^1/_4$ cup (36g) brown or black **sesame seeds**

2 tablespoons (20g) **chia seeds**

$^1/_2$ cup (90g) vegan keto-friendly **chocolate chips**

$^3/_4$ cup (84g) vegan vanilla **protein powder**

$^3/_4$ cup (150g) granulated **allulose** or granulated keto-friendly sweetener of choice

2 tablespoons (10g) **nutritional yeast flakes**

1 tablespoon (8g) ground **cinnamon** or pumpkin spice

2 teaspoons **baking powder**

1 teaspoon **salt**

Notes & Tips ✎

The bars will become very dark brown while baking. However, if your oven runs hot, the temperature may need to be reduced further and the bars baked longer to prevent burning before fully dehydrating.

The ingredients in these bars are costly. If you're concerned that the bars are not fully dehydrated and won't last, freeze them and freshen them up in the oven for 30 to 45 minutes at 200°F (95°C).

For a softer granola bar, bake for only an additional 90 minutes and store refrigerated for up to a week.

Directions

-1- In a medium-sized mixing bowl, whisk together the water, flaxseed meal, almond extract, and vanilla extract. Set aside to gel.

-2- Prepare the walnuts and Brazil nuts as per the ingredient list.

-3- In another medium-sized mixing bowl, whisk together the dry ingredients.

-4- Preheat the oven to 350°F (175°C).

-5- For cookies, line 2 baking sheets with parchment paper.
For bars, prepare 2 baking sheet-sized pieces of parchment paper.

-6- Add the coconut oil and almond butter to the flax mixture and whisk until smooth. Then, add the dry mixture to the wet mixture. Using a silicone spatula or mixing spoon, mix until a thick dough has formed and no dry patches remain.

-7- For cookies, divide the dough into 40 pieces of roughly 2 tablespoons (27g) each. With your hands, roll the pieces into balls and space these about 3 inches (8cm) apart on the lined baking sheets. Gently press the balls down into cookies about $^3/_8$ inch (1cm) thick.
For bars, place a piece of parchment paper on the countertop. Place half of the dough on the parchment and, using oiled hands, press it out into a large rectangle about $^3/_8$ inch (1cm) thick. Then, using a large kitchen knife, cut the rectangle into 10 bars. Wipe the knife blade between cuts to prevent sticking. Repeat this process with the other half of the dough. Transfer the bars, still on the pieces of parchment, to 2 baking sheets.

-8- Place the baking sheets in the center of the oven.
Bake cookies, for 10 to 12 minutes, or until the edges are dark golden brown.
Bake bars, at 350°F (175°C) for 8 minutes and then turn the oven temperature down to 200°F (95°C) and bake for an additional 5 hours, or until fully dehydrated. To determine if the bars are fully dehydrated, break off a piece and allow it to cool fully before testing it. The bars may remain slightly chewy in the center, but should no longer be moist. Keep in mind that the bars nearer to the middle may be less dehydrated than those along the outer edges. Bars must be fully dehydrated to last up to month (or longer) in storage. ✎

-9- Remove the cookies/bars from the oven and allow them to cool on the pans for 5 minutes. Then, transfer them to a wire cooling rack for another 5 to 10 minutes. Be gentle when transferring the cookies.

-10- Enjoy warm or at room temperature.

Almond Joy **frappé**

Yield 1 frappé

Macros Ⓜ 539 calories | 33g protein | 41g fat | 9.2g net carbs ✎

Prep 10 minutes

Equipment required a blender

Store in a well-insulated thermos cup for up to 2 hours.

Fruit-Tea **smoothie**

Yield 1 smoothie

Macros Ⓜ approx. 183 calories | 18g protein | 5.5g fat ✎
blackberry: 7.2g net carbs
raspberry: 8.5g net carbs
strawberry: 8.6g net carbs

Prep 10 minutes, not including time to freeze tea

Equipment required a blender and an ice cube tray (optional)

Store in a well-insulated thermos cup for up to 2 hours.

Almond Joy Frappé Ingredients

1 cup (about 150g) **ice cubes**

$^{1}/_{2}$ cup (120ml) **soy** or **pea milk**

$^{1}/_{2}$ cup (120ml) canned full-fat **coconut milk**

$^{1}/_{4}$ cup (28g) very low-carb chocolate, coconut, or vanilla-flavored **protein powder**

$1^{1}/_{2}$ tablespoons (8g) **cocoa/cacao powder**

$1^{1}/_{2}$ tablespoons (23g) **almond butter**

$^{1}/_{2}$ teaspoon **almond extract**

Almond Joy Frappé Directions

-1- Put all ingredients in a blender and blend to smooth.

-2- Enjoy icy cold.

Allergen-Free Options

coconut-free: replace the coconut milk with very low-carb plant-based cooking cream (Ⓜ will vary). Or, increase the milk to 1 cup (240ml) and the almond butter to 3 tablespoons (47g). Ⓜ 41 PRO | 34 FAT

nut-free: replace the almond butter with sunflower seed butter and omit the almond extract. Ⓜ 7.8 NC

Note: macro notes are per serving and are only provided when and where the difference from the original recipe macros exceeds 10%.

Fruit-Tea Smoothie Ingredients

1 **berry-flavored tea bag** and $^{2}/_{3}$ cup (160ml) boiled **water**, steeped and made into ice cubes <u>OR</u> 1 cup (about 150g) **ice cubes**

$^{3}/_{4}$ cup (180ml) **soy** or **pea milk**

2 tablespoons (14g) very low-carb vanilla or berry-flavored **protein powder**

4 ounces (113g) fresh low-sugar **berries**, such as:

- **blackberries** (about $^{3}/_{4}$ cup)
- **raspberries** (about 1 cup)
- **strawberries** (about $^{3}/_{4}$ cup quartered berries)

Fruit-Tea Smoothie Directions

-1- Steep the tea in the boiled water for about 10 minutes. Remove the tea bag, gently squeeze out the excess liquid, and pour the tea into an ice cube tray. Freeze. This will take 4 to 5 hours.

-2- Put all ingredients in a blender and blend to smooth.

-3- Enjoy icy cold.

Higher Calorie/Fat Option

Add 2 scoops (20g) MCT oil powder, or 1 tablespoon (15ml) coconut or MCT oil to your smoothie.
Ⓜ approx. 305 CALS | 18 to19 FAT

Carb Booster Options

Use blueberries (about $^{3}/_{4}$ cup). Ⓜ 16 NC

Note: macro notes are per serving and are only provided when and where the difference from the original recipe macros exceeds 10%.

Notes & Tips

On a keto diet, an ideal protein powder will have no more than roughly 1g net carbs per 10g of protein. There are protein powders available with 0g net carbs. A typical protein powder contains about 20g of protein per scoop. Some products, like Vega Sport, have larger scoops and thus more protein per scoop.

The macros for this recipe are calculated using Vega Sport Vanilla protein powder and fresh fruit. Oddly, national nutritional data for some frozen fruits can show significantly higher net carbs for an equal weight. That said, feel free to use frozen fruit and skip the fruit-tea ice cubes. Whether you then use the nutritional data for fresh or frozen berries is at your discretion.

On a ketogenic diet, particularly one with a low carb limit, fruit smoothies can be rather disappointing. With less fruit or more protein powder than I've suggested here, I find the natural flavor of the fruit to be too subtle to be worth the carbs.

Celestial Seasonings makes some good fruit-flavored teas. Wild Berry Zinger is a nice option for this smoothie.

FLAX & FILL-IN-THE-BLANK **bread**

YIELD 6 servings of 2 slices each, totalling 12 slices

MACROS Ⓜ (per serving)

almond flour: 224 calories | 6.6g protein | 18g fat | 2.0g net carbs
lupin flour: 175 calories | 9.4g protein | 12g fat | 1.3g net carbs
peanut flour: 202 calories | 12g protein | 12g fat | 2.5g net carbs
sesame flour: 199 calories | 11g protein | 13g fat | 3.3g net carbs
extra flaxseed meal + protein powder: 206 calories | 10g protein | 15g fat | 0.9g net carbs

PREP 30 minutes, 15 minutes of which is inactive | **BAKE** 50 minutes | **COOL** 1 hour

STORE at room temperature for up to 48 hours, or refrigerated for up to a week.

⚠ *Keto baking can be very finicky. I strongly suggest weighing your flours, flaxseed meal, psyllium husks, xanthan gum, and water (ml = g) for this recipe.*

Dry Ingredients

3/4 cup (90g) **flaxseed meal**, preferably golden

3/4 cup (90g) one of the following flours, sifted if lumpy:

- **almond flour**
- **lupin flour**
- defatted **peanut flour**
- defatted **sesame flour**

or 1/4 cup + 2 tablespoons (45g) **flaxseed meal** and 1/4 cup + 2 tablespoons (42g) plain pea **protein powder** and reduce salt to 1/4 teaspoon

1/4 cup + 3 tablespoons (35g) whole **psyllium husks**

1 tablespoon (5g) **nutritional yeast flakes**

2 teaspoons **baking powder**

1 teaspoon (3g) **xanthan gum** ✎

1/2 teaspoon **salt**

Wet Ingredients

warm **water** as follows:

- almond flour or peanut flour:
  1 cup + 1 tablespoon (255ml)
- lupin flour or flaxseed meal + protein powder:
  1 cup + 2 tablespoons (270ml)
- sesame flour: 1 cup + 3 tablespoons (285ml)

2 tablespoons (30ml) light **olive oil** or neutral-flavored oil of choice

1 tablespoon (15ml) **apple cider vinegar** or vinegar of choice

Carb Booster Options

Use 3/4 cup (90g) chickpea flour as your flour option and 1 cup + 2 tablespoons (270ml) warm water.
Ⓜ 196 CALS | 6.8 PRO | 12 FAT | 7.8 NC

Directions

-1- In a medium-sized mixing bowl, whisk together the dry ingredients.

-2- In another medium-sized mixing bowl, whisk together the water, oil, and vinegar. Then, add the dry mixture to the wet mixture. Without delay, using a silicone spatula or mixing spoon, thoroughly mix until no dry patches remain. Allow the dough to rest in the bowl for 2 to 3 minutes.

-3- With oiled hands, form the dough into a small 6-inch (15cm) long loaf (or loaf of desired shape) and place it on a baking sheet. Allow the loaf to rest for 15 minutes. With a sharp knife, score 3-4 shallow slices in the loaf's top.

-4- While the loaf rests, preheat the oven to 375°F (190°C).

-5- Place the loaf in the center of the oven and bake for 50 minutes.

-6- Transfer the loaf from the baking sheet to a wire cooling rack and allow it to cool for at least an hour. Insufficiently cooled bread will seem underbaked.

-7- Slice the loaf into 12 pieces. A baked loaf that is 7 inches (18cm) long, could be sliced as follows: slice the boot ends off as 1-inch (2.5cm) slices and slice the remainder into ten 1/2-inch (12mm) slices.

-8- Enjoy at room temperature or toasted. To prevent the bread from becoming slimy, top it with wet ingredients only when ready to eat.

To make croutons

Preheat the oven to 260°F (125°C). Slice and cube the fully cooled bread. Place the cubes in a single layer on a rimmed baking sheet. Bake for 90 minutes, or until fully dehydrated. A full loaf will make roughly 3 1/2 cups (260g) of croutons.

Notes & Tips ✎

If you'd like to top your loaf with seeds, I'd suggest putting the seeds on a plate, lightly wetting the loaf's top/sides, and pressing the loaf's surface into the seeds.

If you notice a little grit in your bread, this is the psyllium husk. It's normal.

Xanthan gum can be replaced with an additional 2 tablespoons (10g) psyllium husks. However, this will result in the psyllium husk taste being more pronounced, the dough less pliable, and the bread a little denser.

***Troubleshooting:** an ideal loaf, once fully cooled, should have tiny air pockets throughout, giving it an evenly soft and springy texture. A loaf made without enough water will rise less and be a bit drier and denser, with fewer or tinier air pockets. A loaf made with too much water will have larger air pockets at the top and be denser at the loaf's base. Small amounts of water can make a significant difference to the outcome. The water measurements I've provided are what has worked best in my kitchen and with my chosen products. You may need to tweak the recipe to suit your conditions. If doing so, I'd suggest adjusting the water in the recipe by not more than a tablespoon or two at a time.*

HEMP & PUMPKIN SEED **crackers**

YIELD 12 servings of 4 crackers (32g) each, totalling 48 crackers (389g)

MACROS Ⓜ (per serving) 176 calories | 11g protein | 13g fat | 1.3g net carbs

PREP 25 minutes | **BAKE** 1 hour and 30 minutes | **COOL** 10 minutes

EQUIPMENT REQUIRED a small food-processor, a rolling pin, and 2 medium-sized baking sheets

STORE completely dehydrated and fully cooled, at room temperature, for up to a month.

Wet Ingredients

1 cup (240ml) room temperature **water**

$^{1}/_{4}$ cup (40g) **chia seeds**

2 tablespoons (30ml) light **olive oil** or neutral-flavored oil of choice

Dry Ingredients

1 cup (160g) **pumpkin seeds**

$^{1}/_{2}$ cup (80g) **hemp hearts**

$^{1}/_{4}$ cup (28g) plain pea **protein powder**

$^{1}/_{4}$ cup (20g) whole **psyllium husks**

$^{1}/_{4}$ cup (20g) **nutritional yeast flakes**

1 tablespoon (3g) **Herbes de Provence** or Italian seasoning (optional)

$1^{1}/_{2}$ teaspoons **baking powder**

$^{1}/_{2}$ teaspoon ground **black pepper**

$^{1}/_{2}$ teaspoon **salt**

Notes & Tips ✎

If your oven runs hot, the baking temperature may need to be reduced, and the crackers baked longer, to prevent burning or an acrid over-toasted flavor from developing before the crackers are fully dehydrated.

The ingredients in these crackers are costly. If you're concerned that the crackers are not fully dehydrated and won't last, freeze them and freshen them up in the oven for 20 to 25 minutes at 200°F (95°C).

A rolling pin with spacers/thickness guides is a great kitchen tool to have for this recipe. Super Kitchen makes one with a 5mm ($^{1}/_{5}$-inch) option.

Directions

-1- In a medium-sized mixing bowl, whisk together the water and chia seeds. Set aside to gel.

-2- Place the dry ingredients in a small food processor and pulse until the pumpkin seeds are breadcrumb-sized.

-3- Whisk the oil into the chia seed gel and then add the wet mixture to the food processor. Pulse to form a dough and then transfer the dough, and any unincorporated dry ingredients, back to the wet ingredient bowl. Using a silicone spatula or mixing spoon, mix until no dry patches remain.

-4- Preheat the oven to 270°F (130°C).

-5- Prepare 3 baking sheet-sized pieces of parchment paper.

-6- Place a piece of parchment paper on the countertop. Transfer half of the dough to the parchment. With oiled hands, press the dough out into a large rectangle about $^{1}/_{2}$ inch (1cm) thick. Top the dough with another sheet of parchment and, using a rolling pin, roll it out to about $^{1}/_{5}$ inch (5mm) thick. Using a large kitchen knife, cut the dough into $2^{1}/_{8}$-inch (5.5cm) squares, or preferred cracker size/shape. Wipe the knife blade between cuts to prevent sticking. Reusing the top piece of parchment and the remaining piece, repeat the process with the other half of the dough. Transfer the crackers, still on the pieces of parchment, to 2 baking sheets.

-7- Place the baking sheets in the center of the oven and bake for 1 hour and 30 minutes, or until fully dehydrated. To determine if the crackers are fully dehydrated, break off a piece and allow it to cool fully before testing it. Keep in mind that the crackers in the center may be less dehydrated than those at the edges. The crackers must be fully dehydrated to last up to month (or longer) in storage. ✎

-8- Remove the crackers from the oven and allow them to cool on the pans for 5 minutes. Then, transfer them to a wire cooling rack to cool for an additional 5 to 10 minutes.

-9- Break the crackers apart, divide them into 12 servings, and enjoy at room temperature.

Recipe Variations

Sesame & Pumpkin Seed Crackers: replace the hemp hearts with $^{1}/_{2}$ cup (72g) brown or black sesame seeds. Ⓜ 9.3 PRO | 1.9 NC

Note: macro notes are per serving and are only provided when and where the difference from the original recipe macros exceeds 10%.

Cream of Vary-the-Vegetable **soup**

Yield 3 servings of roughly 1 1/3 cups (330g) each, totalling 4 cups (990g)

Macros Ⓜ (per serving)

asparagus: 211 calories | 6.0 protein | 18g fat | 4.1g net carbs

broccolini: 222 calories | 7.0g protein | 18g fat | 3.6g net carbs

celery: 204 calories | 4.8g protein | 18g fat | 3.3g net carbs

mushroom: 210 calories | 6.3g protein | 18g fat | 3.7g net carbs

zucchini: 209 calories | 5.3g protein | 18g fat | 4.3g net carbs

Prep & Cook 45 minutes

Equipment required a heat-safe countertop or immersion blender

Store refrigerated for up to 5 days. Reheat gently on low heat.

Ingredients

8 ounces (227g) one of the following, diced:

- **celery** (about 2 1/4 cups)
- **broccolini®** (about 2 1/2 cups)
- **mushrooms** (about 3 cups)
- **asparagus** (about 2 cups)
- **zucchini** (about 1 medium zucchini or 2 cups)

1 medium stalk (40g) **celery**, diced (about 1/3 cup) ✎

2 medium (36g) **mushrooms**, diced (about 1/2 cup) ✎

1/4 medium (30g) **red bell pepper**, diced (about 1/4 cup)

1/4 medium (28g) **onion**, diced (a scant 1/4 cup)

1 clove (3g) **garlic**, crushed (1/2 teaspoon)

2 tablespoons (30ml) light **olive oil** or neutral-flavored oil of choice

1 teaspoon **Herbes de Provence** or Italian seasoning

a pinch of crushed **red pepper flakes** (optional)

1 **bay leaf**

2 cups (480ml) **vegetable broth** or
1 **bouillon cube** and 2 cups **water** ✎

1 tablespoon (5g) **nutritional yeast flakes**

1/2 teaspoon **tamari**, soy sauce, or aminos

1/4 teaspoon vegan **Worcestershire sauce** (optional)

3/4 cup (180ml) **soy** or **pea milk**

3 scoops (30g) vegan **MCT oil powder** ✎
or 1 1/2 tablespoons (23ml) light olive oil or neutral-flavored oil of choice

Carb Booster Options

For the main vegetable, use broccoli (about 2 1/2 cups) or green beans (about 2 cups).

Ⓜ 221 CALS | 6.5 PRO | 18 FAT | 5.8 NC or

Ⓜ 219 CALS | 5.7 PRO | 18 FAT | 5.9 NC

Directions

-1- Prepare the vegetables and mushrooms as per the ingredient list.

-2- In a medium-sized saucepan, heat the oil on medium-low heat. When hot, add the onion, garlic, Herbes de Provence, and red pepper flakes. Cook for 4 to 5 minutes, or until onions are soft but not brown. Stir frequently and adjust heat as necessary.

-3- Add the remaining vegetables, the mushrooms, and the bay leaf. Increase the heat to medium, cover with a well-fitted lid, and cook for an additional 5 minutes. Stir occasionally. If you're using a fat-based bouillon cube and water for the broth, you can add the cube now to melt it.

-4- Add the broth (or water), nutritional yeast, tamari, and Worcestershire sauce. Replace the lid and bring to a simmer. Simmer for 10 minutes, or until vegetables are tender.

-5- Remove the saucepan from the heat, remove the bay leaf, and transfer roughly three quarters of the soup to a heat-safe blender. Add the milk and MCT oil powder and blend to smooth. Make sure to start the blender at the lowest speed setting and increase to maximum speed gradually. ✎

-6- Return the puréed soup to the saucepan and stir until fully incorporated. Reheat on low if necessary.

-7- Divide the soup equally between 3 soup bowls and enjoy hot.

Notes & Tips ✎

For safety, if using a countertop blender, it is important to use one that allows you to start blending at a very slow blade speed and increase gradually. This may be done via a speed dial, or the machine might have a built-in function for this. Blenders with push-button controls that "jump" into action can result in hot soup being thrown all over you and your kitchen. In addition, to prevent an explosion from steam building up inside the carafe, keep the center plug of the blender lid ajar, or cover the hole with a thickly folded dish towel and your hand. Do not use a bullet-style blender to blend the soup unless it has completely cooled first.

If making Cream of Celery soup, omit the small amount of celery found later in the ingredient list. Likewise for the Cream of Mushroom soup and the small amount of mushroom found later in the ingredient list.

Soup broths can be surprisingly high in net carbs. Check your labels. Edward & Sons make some decent very low-carb bouillon cubes.

Using MCT oil powder adds a particular creaminess and mouthfeel to the soup. However, it's not essential. Another option, apart from the oil one given, is to replace the soy/pea milk with full-fat canned coconut milk. This will add roughly 30 calories, 4g fat, and 1g net carbs per serving, depending on the product used.

MULTI-OPTION **minestrone**

YIELD 5 servings of roughly $1^1/_2$ cups (380g) each, totalling $7^1/_2$ cups (1,900g)

MACROS Ⓜ (per serving) 251 calories | 13g protein | 17g fat | 7.4g net carbs

PREP & COOK 50 minutes, not including time to cook soybeans

EQUIPMENT REQUIRED a countertop or immersion blender

STORE refrigerated for up to 5 days. Reheat gently on low heat.

Broth Ingredients

4 ounces (113g) **mushrooms**, chopped or sliced (about 1 1/2 cups)

1/2 medium (55g) **onion**, diced (about 1/3 cup)

2 cloves (6g) **garlic**, crushed (1 teaspoon)

1/4 cup (60ml/54g) light **olive oil** or neutral-flavored oil of choice

1 teaspoon **Herbes de Provence** or Italian seasoning

1/2 teaspoon crushed **red pepper flakes** (optional or to taste)

4 cups (960ml) **vegetable broth** or
2 **bouillon cubes** and 4 cups **water** ✎

2 tablespoons (33g) **tomato paste**

2 tablespoons (10g) **nutritional yeast flakes**

1 teaspoon ground **cumin**

1/4 teaspoon **onion powder**

1/8 teaspoon **garlic powder**

1/8 teaspoon ground **black pepper**

Other Ingredients

1 1/2 cups (258g) cooked **soybeans**

1 medium stalk (40g) **celery**, diced (about 1/3 cup)

1 medium (61g) **carrot** or 1/2 medium (61g) **turnip**, diced (about 1/2 cup)

1/2 cup (60g) one of the following, diced:

- **green beans** (about 10 pieces)
- **wax beans** (about 10 pieces)
- **zucchini** (about 1/3 medium)
- **cauliflower** (about 1/4 small head)

1 cup (246g) canned **diced tomatoes** (fire-roasted are a great option if available to you)

1/2 teaspoon dried **thyme**

1/2 teaspoon dried **oregano**

1 **bay leaf**

2 cups (60g) baby **spinach**

Directions

-1- Prepare the mushrooms, onion, and garlic found in the "Broth Ingredients" section, and the celery and chosen vegetables found in the "Other Ingredients" section, as per the details in the ingredient list.

-2- In a large saucepan, heat the oil on medium heat. When hot, add the mushrooms, onion, garlic, Herbes de Provence, and red pepper flakes. Cook for 6 to 7 minutes, or until the onions are soft but not brown, and the mushrooms are tender. Stir frequently and adjust heat as necessary.

-3- Meanwhile, put the remaining broth ingredients in a blender.

-4- Remove the saucepan from the heat and transfer the cooked mixture to the blender. Blend to smooth.

-5- Return the blended mixture to the saucepan and add all remaining ingredients apart from the spinach. Cover with a well-fitted lid and bring to a simmer on medium heat. Reduce the heat as necessary and simmer for 10 to 15 minutes, or until vegetables are tender.

-6- Add the spinach and simmer for 2 minutes, or until the spinach is wilted.

-7- Remove the bay leaf. Divide the soup equally between 5 soup bowls and enjoy hot.

Allergen-Free Options

soy-free (but higher carb): replace the soybeans with a 15-ounce (425g) can of cannellini beans, drained (about 1 1/2 cups [269g]). Ⓜ 8.8g PRO | 13g FAT | 15g NC

Carb Booster Options

Add 1/2 medium (107g) potato (diced - about 3/4 cup) alongside the other ingredients. Increase the simmer time to 15 to 20 minutes. Ⓜ 11 NC

Add 1/2 cup (61g) elbow pasta. Either pre-cook the pasta and add it near the end of the simmering time to heat through, or add it dry with the other ingredients and cook until tender (add extra water if necessary). Ⓜ 296 CALS | 15 PRO | 16 NC

Add 1/2 cup (101g) cooked brown rice alongside the other ingredients. Ⓜ 12 NC

Notes & Tips ✎

Any combination of the vegetable options given in the recipe will result in similar macros. The macros given with the recipe are an average of the options.

Storebought soup broths can be surprisingly high in net carbs. Check your labels. Edward & Sons make some decent very low-carb bouillon cubes.

Minestrone often contains pasta or rice. I have tried this recipe with edamame pasta, chickpea pasta, and kelp noodles. I don't recommend any of these options.

Note: macro notes are per serving and are only provided when and where the difference from the original recipe macros exceeds 10%.

LEMON GARLIC **spinach**

YIELD 4 salads | dressing: $^3/_4$ cup (180ml), equal to 12 tablespoons (3 tablespoons [45ml] per salad)

MACROS Ⓜ (per dressed salad) 207 calories | 4.8g protein | 19g fat | 5.4g net carbs
(per tablespoon of dressing) 57 calories | 0.2g protein | 6.0g fat | 1.1g net carbs

PREP 15 minutes

EQUIPMENT REQUIRED a very large mixing bowl (optional - multiple smaller bowls can be used)

STORE dressing and spinach separately, both refrigerated, for up to 3 days.

Dressing Ingredients

1/3 cup (80ml/71g) light **olive oil** or neutral-flavored oil of choice

1/3 cup (80ml) **lemon juice** (about 2 medium lemons)

8 cloves (24g) **garlic**, crushed ✎ (1 tablespoon + 1 teaspoon)

2 teaspoons dried **oregano**

1 teaspoon **salt**

Salad Ingredients

20 cups (600g) baby **spinach**

Directions

-1- Put all dressing ingredients in a leakproof container and shake to combine. Or, whisk the ingredients together in a small bowl. Set aside.

-2- Prepare the spinach and put it in a very large mixing bowl. If you don't own a very large mixing bowl, you may need to dress the spinach in parts. Top the spinach with the dressing and use your hands to massage the dressing into the spinach until it's fully coated and somewhat wilted. This will only take a couple of minutes to achieve. The spinach will reduce greatly in size.

-3- Divide the spinach equally between 4 dinner bowls.

-4- Enjoy soon after dressing. To make this salad a full meal, see some options for protein-rich toppings and sides below.

Notes & Tips ✎

This salad is very garlicky and tangy, burn your mouth level garlicky. I love this about it, but you may not. If this does not sound appealing to you, reduce the garlic by at least half. Doing this also reduces the net carbs in the full recipe by 3.7g. You could replace these carbs with 6 medium (72g) strawberries (diced - about 1/2 cup) sprinkled on your salad.

The yield and macros for the Bacony Bits recipe will vary with the product used. See Bacony Bits notes.

The weight given for tofu is pressed weight. However, most tofu comes packed in water and weighs more. By my calculation, an unpressed serving of extra-firm tofu weighs roughly 105g.

Protein-rich toppings or sides

- Hemp & Pumpkin Seed Crackers | Page 30 | Ⓜ 176 CALS | 11 PRO | 13 FAT | 1.3 NC
- Flax & Lupin Bread | Page 28 | Ⓜ 175 CALS | 9.4 PRO | 12 FAT | 1.3 NC
- Flax & Protein Powder Bread | Page 28 | Ⓜ 206 CALS | 10 PRO | 15 FAT | 0.9 NC
- Seasoned Air Fryer Tofu | Page 56 | Ⓜ 191 CALS | 15 PRO | 12 FAT | 1.6 NC
- Bacony Bits - 2 servings ✎ | Page 72 |
  (pea-based) Ⓜ 58 CALS | 5.2 PRO | 3.8 FAT | 0.4 NC
  (soy-based) Ⓜ 54 CALS | 3.6 PRO | 3.5 FAT | 1.3 NC
- Brami lupini beans - a single-serve packet (65g) Ⓜ 78 CALS | 8.5 PRO | 2.0 FAT | 0.0 NC
- edamame, dry-roasted, Seapoint Farms - a snack pack (22.5g) Ⓜ 98 CALS | 11 PRO | 3.8 FAT | 2.3 NC
- edamame, shelled, frozen - 1/4 cup (35g) Ⓜ 38 CALS | 3.9 PRO | 1.7 FAT | 1.0 NC
- hemp hearts - 2 tablespoons (20g) Ⓜ 122 CALS | 7.0 PRO | 10 FAT | 0.4 NC
- pumpkin seeds - 2 tablespoons (20g) Ⓜ 118 CALS | 7.2 PRO | 8.9 FAT | 1.0 NC
- soybeans, cooked - 1/4 cup (43g) Ⓜ 74 CALS | 7.8 PRO | 3.9 FAT | 0.9 NC
- tofu, extra-firm - a serving (85g ✎) Ⓜ 70 CALS | 8.0 PRO | 3.5 FAT | 0.0 NC

Nuts and other seeds are also rich in protein. See page 21 for their macro details.

Note: macros in the Protein-rich toppings or sides section above do not include the Lemon Garlic Spinach. Macros for the recipes included in this section are per serving unless stated otherwise.

BROCCOLI & CAULIFLOWER **salad**

YIELD 4 salads | dressing: $^3/_4$ cup + 2 tablespoons (210ml), equal to 14 tablespoons ($3^1/_2$ tablespoons [53ml] per salad)

MACROS Ⓜ (per dressed salad) 454 calories | 18g protein | 37g fat | 8.4g net carbs
(per tablespoon of dressing) 65 calories | 0.5g protein | 6.8g fat | 0.3g net carbs

PREP 30 minutes | **MARINATE** 1 hour (this time can be used to make the Bacony Bits)

STORE dressed salad refrigerated for up to 24 hours. Or, store dressing and veggie mixture separately, both refrigerated, for up to 3 days. Dressed or undressed, store seeds and Bacony Bits separately from wet/moist components, at room temperature, to maintain crunch.

Dressing Ingredients

1/2 cup + 1 tablespoon (135ml/124g) vegan **mayonnaise**

2 tablespoons (30g) **Dijon mustard**

1 1/2 tablespoons (23ml) **apple cider vinegar** or vinegar of choice

1 1/2 tablespoons (8g) **nutritional yeast flakes**

1 tablespoon (13g) granulated **allulose** or equivalent in keto-friendly sweetener of choice

1 clove (3g) **garlic**, crushed (1/2 teaspoon)

1/4 teaspoon **salt**

Salad Ingredients

1/2 cup (80g) **pumpkin seeds**, toasted

3 1/2 cups (319g) chopped **broccoli** (about 1 medium crown or a 12-ounce bag of florets)

3 cups (321g) chopped **cauliflower** (about 1/2 medium head or a 12-ounce bag of florets)

1/4 medium (28g) **onion**, preferably red, thinly sliced (a scant 1/4 cup)

1/2 batch (40g) **Bacony Bits** | Page 72 | (about 1/2 cup ✎)

Directions

-1- Preheat the oven to 350°F (175°C). Spread the pumpkin seeds out in a rimmed baking sheet and toast them for 5 to 7 minutes. Monitor to prevent burning. Allow the seeds to cool once toasted.

-2- Meanwhile, in a small bowl, gently whisk together the dressing ingredients. Set aside.

-3- Prepare the broccoli, cauliflower, and onion as per the ingredient list. Transfer the prepared veggies to a medium-sized mixing bowl.

-4- Drizzle the vegetables with the dressing. Using a large silicone spatula or mixing spoon, mix thoroughly, until all vegetables are well-coated with dressing. Cover the bowl and refrigerate the salad for about an hour. If you have not already prepared the Bacony Bits, this can be done now.

-5- Add the toasted pumpkin seeds to the salad and mix to distribute them throughout.

-6- Divide the salad equally between 4 dinner bowls and top each with the Bacony Bits, 2 tablespoons (10g) per salad.

-7- Enjoy soon after adding the pumpkin seeds and Bacony Bits.

Notes & Tips ✎

The yield of the Bacony Bits recipe will vary with the product used. A half batch may be less than 1/2 cup, and thus less than 2 tablespoons per salad. However, the weight given should remain the same.

Raw broccoli and cauliflower can cause digestive upset for some people. To mitigate this, you can steam the florets briefly (2 to 3 minutes). Cool the florets fully before chopping them for the salad.

Dried cranberries have added sugar or apple juice to negate their tartness and keep them chewy. Some brands use less sweetening agent than others. Two possible lower-carb brands to look for are Food to Live (North America) and Forest Feast (UK).

Recipe Variations

All broccoli: omit the cauliflower and increase the broccoli to 7 cups (637g), equal to about 2 medium crowns or two 12-ounce bags of florets. Ⓜ 9.2 NC

Go Beyond: omit the Bacony Bits and top the salad with 4 Beyond Breakfast Sausage links, cooked as directed and then diced.

Carb Booster Options

Add 1/4 cup + 2 tablespoons (54g) raisins or 1/3 cup (53g) dried cranberries. If the cranberries are on the larger side, I'd suggest cutting them in half for better distribution throughout the salad. I use kitchen scissors for this. Ⓜ 19 NC ✎

Note: macro notes are per serving and are only provided when and where the difference from the original recipe macros exceeds 10%. Both carb-booster options have 19g net carbs.

UNCONVENTIONAL **tabbouleh**

YIELD 4 salads | dressing: $^{1}/_{2}$ cup (120ml), equal to 8 tablespoons (2 tablespoons [30ml] per salad)

MACROS Ⓜ (per dressed salad) 542 calories | 22g protein | 46g fat | 8.4g net carbs
(per tablespoon of dressing) 62 calories | 0.1g protein | 6.8g fat | 0.6g net carbs

PREP 30 minutes, not including time to cook and cool cauliflower rice (recipe available on page 76)

STORE dressing and undressed salad separately, both refrigerated, for up to 2 days.

Dressing Ingredients

$^1/_4$ cup (60ml/54g) light **olive oil** or neutral-flavored oil of choice

$^1/_4$ cup (60ml) **lemon juice** (about 1 large lemon)

1 clove (3g) **garlic**, crushed ($^1/_2$ teaspoon)

1 teaspoon **salt**

Salad Ingredients

4 cups (120g) baby **spinach**, finely chopped

2 cups (260g) cooked and cooled **cauliflower rice** (about $^1/_2$ medium head)

1 cup (50g) finely chopped flatleaf **parsley** (about one 2-ounce bunch)

2 medium (30g) **green onions**, chopped (about $^1/_2$ cup)

1 large or $1^1/_2$ medium (185g) **tomatoes**, diced (about 1 cup)

$^1/_2$ medium (150g) English **cucumber**, diced (about 1 cup)

$^1/_2$ cup (68g) sliced black **olives**

$1^1/_4$ cups (200g) **hemp hearts**

$^1/_4$ cup (36g) brown or black **sesame seeds**

Directions

-1- Put all dressing ingredients in a leakproof container and shake to combine. Or, whisk the ingredients together in a small bowl. Set aside.

-2- Prepare the remaining ingredients as per the ingredient list.

-3- Combine the salad ingredients in a large mixing bowl, cover with the dressing, and toss to coat thoroughly.

-4- Divide the salad equally between 4 dinner bowls.

-5- Enjoy soon after dressing.

Notes & Tips ✎

Check your Middle Eastern supermarket for chopped parsley. It's very common in the UAE where I live. Pomegranate arils removed from the fruit may also be available in a Middle Eastern supermarket.

Green olives have fewer net carbs than black olives, and peeled cucumber has fewer net carbs than unpeeled. If you want to reduce the carbs in the recipe a little, you could make these swaps. M 7.3 NC

Recipe Variations

More traditional tabbouleh: omit the spinach, triple the parsley to 3 cups (150g), and add a handful of fresh mint leaves, finely chopped.

Carb Booster Options

Add $^1/_2$ cup (80g) pomegranate arils. M 11 NC

Reduce the cauliflower rice to 1 cup (130g) and the hemp hearts to 1 cup + 2 tablespoons (180g). Add 1 cooked and cooled cup of either quinoa (185g) or bulgur wheat (182g). M 18 NC or M 16 NC

Note: macro notes are per serving and are only provided when and where the difference from the original recipe macros exceeds 10%.

LUPINI CAESAR **salad**

YIELD 4 salads | dressing: 1 cup + 2 tablespoons (270ml), equal to 18 tablespoons ($4^1/_2$ tablespoons [68ml] per salad)

MACROS Ⓜ (per dressed salad) 419 calories | 14g protein | 36g fat | 4.9g net carbs
(per tablespoon of dressing) 55 calories | 0.8g protein | 5.5g fat | 0.5g net carbs

PREP 20 minutes, not including time to make Flax & Lupin Bread croutons or Bacony Bits

EQUIPMENT REQUIRED a high-powered blender

STORE dressing and chopped Romaine separately, both refrigerated, for up to 4 days.
Store shaved nuts, croutons, and Bacony Bits separately from wet/moist components, at room temperature, to maintain crunch.

Dressing Ingredients

$^1/_3$ cup (80ml) **soy** or **pea milk**

$^1/_4$ cup (60ml/54g) light **olive oil** or neutral-flavored oil of choice

$^1/_4$ cup (45g) brined **lupini beans**, rinsed

$1^1/_2$ tablespoons (23ml) **lemon juice** (about $^1/_2$ medium lemon)

$1^1/_2$ teaspoons **Dijon mustard**

3 cloves (9g) **garlic** ($1^1/_2$ teaspoons crushed garlic)

a pinch of **salt**

2 tablespoons (10g) **nutritional yeast flakes**

$^1/_4$ cup (60ml/55g) vegan **mayonnaise**

Salad Ingredients

1 medium head (570g) **Romaine lettuce**, chopped or torn (about 14 cups or two 10-ounce bags)

2 servings **Flax & Lupin Bread** croutons | Page 28 | ($^1/_3$ loaf - about 1 cup of croutons)

$^1/_4$ batch (20g) **Bacony Bits** | Page 72 | (about $^1/_4$ cup ✎)

4 medium (19g) **Brazil nuts**, thinly sliced/shaved

Notes & Tips ✎

If you are using a countertop blender with a large carafe, you may have difficulty blending this dressing. I use the smaller 32-ounce (1-liter) carafe of my Vitamix or my bullet blender.

The yield of the Bacony Bits recipe will vary with the product used. A quarter batch may be less than $^1/_4$ cup, and thus less than 1 tablespoon per salad. However, the weight given should remain the same.

The macros in the salad dressing are prone to significant variation depending on the mayonnaise and lupini beans you use. If accuracy is a concern for you, you may wish to recalculate the macros for this recipe using your products of choice.

To make this salad TVP-free the Bacony Bits could be replaced with 2 Beyond Breakfast Sausage links, cooked as directed and then diced.

Directions

-1- Put all dressing ingredients, apart from the nutritional yeast and mayonnaise, in a high-powered blender and blend to smooth. Add the nutritional yeast and blend briefly to incorporate. Gently whisk in the mayonnaise. If the blended mixture has become warm, put it in the refrigerator to cool before adding the mayonnaise.

-2- Prepare the lettuce and Brazil nuts as per the ingredient list.

-3- Place the lettuce in a large mixing bowl, cover it with the dressing, and toss until the leaves are thoroughly coated.

-4- Add the croutons and toss to distribute them throughout the salad.

-5- Divide the salad equally between 4 dinner bowls and top with the Bacony Bits and Brazil nut shavings, 1 tablespoon (5g) of Bacony Bits and 2 teaspoons of (5g) Brazil nut shavings per bowl.

-6- Enjoy soon after dressing.

Allergen-Free Options

lupini-free: replace the lupini beans in the dressing with either $^1/_4$ cup (43g) cooked and cooled soybeans or 3 tablespoons (30g) pumpkin seeds. If using the pumpkin seed option, add an additional tablespoon (15ml) of milk. For both options, increase the salt to $^1/_4$ teaspoon. Make the croutons with Flax & Protein Powder Bread.

Ⓜ (per dressed salad with soybean dressing) 4.4 NC

Ⓜ (per dressed salad with pumpkin seed dressing) 469 CALS | 15 PRO | 41 FAT

nut-free: replace the Brazil nuts with 2 tablespoons (20g) hemp heart.

Carb Booster Options

Use croutons made with Flax & Chickpea Bread. Ⓜ 8.2 NC

Note: macro notes are per serving and are only provided when and where the difference from the original recipe macros exceeds 10%.

SPICY CABBAGE **slaw**

YIELD 4 salads | dressing: 1/2 cup (120ml), equal to 8 tablespoons (2 tablespoons [30ml] per salad)

MACROS Ⓜ (per dressed salad) 223 calories | 8.0g protein | 16g fat | 7.2g net carbs
(per tablespoon of dressing) 54 calories | 0.7g protein | 5.2g fat | 0.6g net carbs

PREP 30 minutes (or less if using pre-shredded cabbage and pre-toasted pumpkin seeds)

EQUIPMENT REQUIRED a chute-style food processor with a slicing blade to shred the cabbage (optional - can use coleslaw mix or very thinly slice the cabbage by hand or with a mandoline)

STORE dressing and cabbage/green onion mixture separately, both refrigerated, for up to 4 days. Store seeds separately from wet/moist components, at room temperature, to maintain crunch.

Dressing Ingredients

3 tablespoons (45ml) light **olive oil** or vegan mayonnaise or neutral-flavored oil of choice

2 tablespoons (30ml) red or white **wine vinegar** or vinegar of choice

1 tablespoon (15ml) **tamari**, soy sauce, or aminos

2 teaspoons **Dijon mustard**

2 teaspoons **sriracha** or hot sauce of choice

1 clove (3g) **garlic**, crushed (1/2 teaspoon)

2 tablespoons (25g) **allulose** or equivalent in keto-friendly sweetener of choice

1 tablespoon (5g) **nutritional yeast flakes**

1 teaspoon dried **oregano**

1/4 teaspoon ground **black pepper**

1/8 teaspoon **salt**

Salad Ingredients

1/3 cup (53g) **pumpkin seeds**, toasted

8 cups (560g) shredded green **cabbage** or coleslaw mix (about 1/2 medium head or two 10-ounce bags) ✎

2 medium (30g) **green onions**, chopped (about 1/2 cup)

Directions

-1- Preheat the oven to 350°F (175°C). Spread the pumpkin seeds out in a rimmed baking sheet and toast them for 5 to 7 minutes. Monitor to prevent burning. Allow the seeds to cool once toasted.

-2- Meanwhile, put all dressing ingredients in a leakproof container and shake to combine. Or, whisk the ingredients together in a small bowl. If using mayonnaise, shake/whisk gently to prevent the mayonnaise from losing its creamy structure.

-3- Prepare the cabbage and green onion as per the ingredient list.

-4- Put the cabbage, green onion, and pumpkin seeds in a medium-sized mixing bowl, drizzle with the dressing, and toss to coat thoroughly.

-5- Divide the salad equally between 4 dinner bowls.

-6- Enjoy soon after dressing.

Notes & Tips ✎

To make this salad a full meal, see some options for protein-rich toppings and sides on page 37.

Both cabbage and green onions can become bitter when old or once they have been chopped. When time allows, I prefer to make this salad with freshly shredded/chopped items.

Feel free to use a coleslaw mix that includes some red cabbage and carrot. The macros will be similar.

The macro calculation for the broccoli slaw variation uses national nutritional data for broccoli, which appears to roughly align with broccoli slaw label data.

Carb Booster Options

Reduce the green cabbage to 4 cups (280g) (about one 10-ounce bag) and add 3 cups (210g) shredded red cabbage (about one 8-ounce bag) and 2 medium (122g) julienned carrot (about 1 1/2 cups). Ⓜ 9.5 NC

Replace the cabbage with 8 cups (680g) (two 12-ounce bags) of broccoli slaw. Ⓜ 246 CALS | 11 PRO | 9.1 NC

Note: macro notes are per serving and are only provided when and where the difference from the original recipe macros exceeds 10%.

SPICY BEAN & BELL PEPPER **salad**

YIELD 4 salads | dressing: 1/2 cup (120ml), equal to 8 tablespoons (2 tablespoons [30ml] per salad)

MACROS Ⓜ (per dressed salad) 361 calories | 21g protein | 25g fat | 7.7g net carbs
(per tablespoon of dressing) 54 calories | 0.7g protein | 5.2g fat | 0.6g net carbs

PREP 30 minutes

STORE marinating beans and pepper/onion mixture separately, both refrigerated, for up to 3 days. Store seeds separately from wet/moist components, at room temperature, to maintain crunch.

Dressing Ingredients

3 tablespoons (45ml) light **olive oil** or vegan mayonnaise or neutral-flavored oil of choice

2 tablespoons (30ml) red or white **wine vinegar** or vinegar of choice

1 tablespoon (15ml) **tamari**, soy sauce, or aminos

2 teaspoons **Dijon mustard**

2 teaspoons **sriracha** or hot sauce of choice

1 clove (3g) **garlic**, crushed (1/2 teaspoon)

2 tablespoons (25g) **allulose** or equivalent in keto-friendly sweetener of choice

1 tablespoon (5g) **nutritional yeast flakes**

1 teaspoon dried **oregano**

1/4 teaspoon ground **black pepper**

1/8 teaspoon **salt**

Salad Ingredients

1/2 cup (80g) **pumpkin seeds**, toasted

1 1/2 cups (258g) cooked & cooled **soybeans**

3 medium (357g) **bell peppers**, diced ✎ (about 3 cups)

1/4 medium (28g) **onion**, preferably red, diced (a scant 1/4 cup)

Directions

-1- Preheat the oven to 350°F (175°C). Spread the pumpkin seeds out in a rimmed baking sheet and toast them for 5 to 7 minutes. Monitor to prevent burning. Allow the seeds to cool once toasted.

-2- Meanwhile, put all dressing ingredients in a leakproof container and shake to combine. Or, whisk the ingredients together in a small bowl. If using mayonnaise, shake/whisk gently to prevent the mayonnaise from losing its creamy structure.

-3- Put the beans in a medium-sized mixing bowl, cover with the dressing, and mix to fully coat the beans. Cover and set aside in the refrigerator to marinate for 20 to 25 minutes.

-4- Meanwhile, prepare the bell peppers and onion as per the ingredient list.

-5- Add the bell pepper, onion, and pumpkin seeds to the beans and mix to distribute the vegetables and seeds throughout.

-6- Divide the salad equally between 4 dinner bowls.

-7- Enjoy soon after adding the vegetables and pumpkin seeds to the marinated bean mixture.

Allergen-Free Options

soy-free (but higher carb): replace the soybeans with a 15-ounce (425g) can of pinto beans, drained (about 1 1/2 cups [257g]). Ⓜ 15g PRO | 20g FAT | 18g NC

Note: macro notes are per serving and are only provided when and where the difference from the original recipe macros exceeds 10%.

Notes & Tips ✎

The macros for this recipe are calculated with a green pepper, a red pepper, and a yellow pepper. Yellow peppers are higher in carbs that other bell peppers. To reduce the carbs in this recipe, you could use two red peppers and one green, or do a 50/50 split of green and red pepper. This would reduce the net carbs per serving to 7.3g and 7.1g respectively.

HEARTY HOMESTYLE **chili**

YIELD 10 servings of roughly 1 cup (260g) each, totalling 10 cups (2,600g)

MACROS Ⓜ (per serving)
pea-based TVP: 278 calories | 20g protein | 17g fat | 7.7g net carbs
soy-based TVP: 272 calories | 18g protein | 16g fat | 9.2g net carbs

PREP 40 minutes | **COOK** 30 minutes

STORE refrigerated for up to 5 days.

Ingredients

$^{1}/_{2}$ cup (120ml/108g) light **olive oil** or neutral-flavored oil of choice

1 medium (110g) **onion**, diced (about $^{3}/_{4}$ cup)

2 cloves (6g) **garlic**, crushed (1 teaspoon)

8 ounces (227g) **mushrooms**, diced (about 3 cups)

4 medium stalks (160g) **celery**, diced (about $1^{1}/_{2}$ cups)

1 medium (119g) **red bell pepper**, diced (about 1 cup)

$^{1}/_{2}$ cup (70g) pickled **jalapeño slices**, chopped

3.17 ounces (90g) **textured vegetable protein (TVP)** crumbles/ground (equal to 1 to 2 cups ✎) or 1 pound (454g) "fresh" plant-based ground/mince and reduce the oil to $^{1}/_{4}$ cup (60ml/54g)

3 cups (516g) cooked **soybeans**

2 cups (480ml) **water**

1 15-ounce (425g) can **tomato sauce**

1 14.5-ounce (411g) can **diced tomatoes**

2 tablespoons (33g) **tomato paste**

$1^{1}/_{2}$ teaspoons **liquid smoke** (optional)

$^{1}/_{4}$ cup (20g) **nutritional yeast flakes**

2 tablespoons (25g) **allulose** or equivalent in keto-friendly sweetener of choice

1 tablespoon (5g) **cocoa/cacao powder**

2 tablespoons (16g) **chili powder** ✎

2 teaspoons ground **cumin**

1 teaspoon **garlic powder**

1 teaspoon **onion powder**

1 teaspoon **salt**

Carb Booster Options

Add a small 8.5-ounce (241g) can of sugar-free corn, drained (about 1 cup [164g]). Ⓜ 9.7 NC

Directions

-1- Prepare the onion, garlic, mushrooms, celery, red pepper, and jalapeño slices as per the ingredient list.

-2- In a medium-sized pot, heat the oil on medium-low heat. When hot, add the onion and garlic. Cook for 4 to 5 minutes, or until onions are soft but not brown. Stir frequently and adjust heat as necessary. If using a "fresh" plant-based meat instead of TVP, add it now. Increase the heat to medium and fry the meat until browned, about 5 minutes.

-3- Add the mushrooms, celery, and red pepper. Increase the heat to medium, cover with a well-fitted lid, and cook for 5 minutes. Stir occasionally.

-4- Add all remaining ingredients to the pot. Add the TVP unhydrated. Stir well.

-5- Cover, heat to a simmer, and simmer on low heat for at least 30 minutes. Stir occasionally. Monitor and add water if necessary.

-6- Divide the chili equally between 10 bowls.

-7- Enjoy hot.

Allergen-Free Options

soy-free (but higher carb): replace the soybeans with two 15-ounce (425g) cans of kidney beans, drained (about 3 cups [531g]). Ⓜ 15g PRO | 13g FAT | 15g NC

Notes & Tips ✎

Chili powder is a spice blend that is readily available in North America. If this product isn't available to you, you can find a recipe for Chili Powder on page 78.

TVP crumbles and ground/mince come in various sizes and textures, which makes it difficult to provide an exact cup measurement. I use either Plant Boss Meatless Crumbles, which are pea-based, or Bob's Redmill soy-based TVP. I've found 90g of Plant Boss Meatless Crumbles to be roughly 2 cups and Bob's Redmill TVP, which is more like a ground/mince, to be roughly 1 cup. Nutritional profiles also vary quite a bit by product and between pea-based and soy-based options, with soy-based options typically being higher in net carbs and lower in protein. Made with "fresh" Beyond or Impossible Ground, this recipe had about 10g net carbs per serving at the time this book was written.

If you have time to make this chili in advance, I find that the flavors are much richer and well-rounded the next day.

Note: macro notes are per serving and are only provided when and where the difference from the original recipe macros exceeds 10%.

KUNG PAO **beans** on CAULI-HEMP **rice**

YIELD 5 servings

MACROS Ⓜ (per serving) 390 calories | 25g protein | 27g fat | 7.9g net carbs

PREP 30 minutes, not including time to cook soybeans, make cauliflower rice, or make Kung Pao-ish Sauce (recipes for preparing soybeans and cauliflower rice available on page 76)

STORE refrigerated for up to 5 days. Store peanuts separately from wet/moist components, at room temperature, to maintain crunch. Green onion could also be stored separately from reheatable components, refrigerated, to maintain its raw flavor.

Ingredients

$1^1/_2$ cups (258g) cooked **soybeans**

$^1/_3$ batch **Kung Pao-ish Sauce** | Page 66 |
(approx. $^1/_2$ cup [120ml])

8 ounces (227g) **mushrooms**, quartered
(about 3 cups)

1 medium (119g) **red bell pepper**, chopped
(about 1 cup)

1 cup (120g) chopped **green beans**

$2^1/_2$ cups (325g) cooked **cauliflower rice**
(about $^1/_2$ medium-large head)

$^2/_3$ cup (107g) **hemp hearts**

$^1/_2$ cup (72g) oil-roasted **peanuts**, chopped

2 medium (30g) **green onions**, chopped
(about $^1/_2$ cup)

Directions

-1- Put the soybeans and sauce in a small saucepan, cover with a well-fitted lid, and set to warm and marinate on the stovetop over low heat.

-2- Prepare the mushrooms, bell pepper, green beans, peanuts, and green onion as per the ingredient list.

-3- Put a medium-sized sauté pan on the stovetop over medium-low heat. Add the mushrooms, bell pepper, green beans, and the warm bean mixture. Using a silicone spatula or mixing spoon, stir well. Cover with a well-fitted lid, and cook for roughly 8 minutes, or until vegetables are near desired tenderness. Stir occasionally and monitor. Add a splash of water if sauce is becoming too thick.

-4- Meanwhile, heat the cauliflower rice either on the stovetop in a small saucepan using low heat, or in the microwave in a small microwave-safe mixing bowl. Unless the rice you're using is rather wet, add a splash of water before heating it, and then cover the pan/bowl. Once heated, add the hemp hearts to the pan/bowl and mix to distribute them throughout the rice. Divide the rice mixture equally between 5 dinner bowls, a little over $^1/_2$ cup (86g) per bowl.

-5- Remove the lid from the bean mixture and increase the heat to medium. Cook until the vegetables are a desired tenderness and the sauce has somewhat thickened, 3 to 5 minutes. Stir frequently.

-6- Top the rice mixture with equal portions of the bean mixture, about $^3/_4$ cup (165g) per bowl. Sprinkle with the chopped peanuts and green onions, about $1^1/_2$ tablespoons of each per bowl (14g and 6g respectively).

-7- Enjoy hot.

Allergen-Free Options

pea(nut)-free: replace the peanuts with $^1/_2$ cup (65g) slivered almonds or $^1/_2$ cup (80g) pumpkin seeds. For improved crunch and flavor, toast these in a rimmed baking sheet for 6 to 8 minutes at 350°F (175°C).

soy-free (but higher carb): replace the soybeans with a 15-ounce (425g) can of black beans, drained (about $1^1/_2$ cups [258g]). Ⓜ 20g PRO | 23g FAT | 16g NC

Note: macro notes are per serving and are only provided when and where the difference from the original recipe macros exceeds 10%.

Notes & Tips ✎

This dish is somewhat spicy. If you don't enjoy spicy food, reduce or omit the crushed red pepper flakes and black pepper in the Kung Pao-ish Sauce.

Carb Booster Options

Reduce the cauliflower rice to $1^1/_2$ cups (195g) and use one of the following three options: 1) add 1 cup (158g) cooked white rice, or 2) reduce the hemp hearts to $^1/_2$ cup (80g) and add $1^1/_4$ cups (231g) cooked quinoa, or 3) reduce the hemp hearts to $^1/_4$ cup + 2 tablespoons (60g) and add $^1/_2$ cup (100g) chickpea risoni/rice, cooked as per package directions. Ⓜ 16 NC (all options)

BEAN & PUMPKIN CURRY patties

YIELD 10 servings of 1 patty each, totalling 10 patties

MACROS Ⓜ (per serving) 193 calories | 11g protein | 14g fat | 3.8g net carbs

PREP 35 minutes, not including time to cook soybeans | **BAKE** 25 minutes | **FRY** 10 to 15 minutes (optional)

STORE baked or unbaked, refrigerated, for up to 5 days.

Ingredients

2 tablespoons (30ml) **coconut oil** or neutral-flavored oil of choice

$^1/_2$ medium (55g) **onion**, diced (about $^1/_3$ cup)

3 cloves (9g) **garlic**, crushed ($1^1/_2$ teaspoons)

$1^1/_2$ teaspoons (9g) grated fresh **ginger**

$1^1/_2$ cups (258g) cooked **soybeans**

$^1/_2$ cup (123g) canned **pumpkin purée**

$^1/_2$ cup (120ml) canned full-fat **coconut milk**

1 tablespoon (16g) **tomato paste**

1 teaspoon **tamari**, soy sauce, or aminos

1 tablespoon (5g) **nutritional yeast flakes**

1 teaspoon **curry powder**

$^1/_2$ teaspoon crushed **red pepper flakes** (optional or to taste) or a thinly sliced Jwala chili pepper

$^1/_4$ teaspoon **garam masala**

$^1/_4$ teaspoon **onion powder**

$^1/_4$ teaspoon **garlic powder**

$^1/_2$ + $^1/_4$ teaspoon **salt**

$^1/_2$ cup (50g) **walnuts**, roughly chopped

$^1/_4$ cup (40g) **hemp hearts**

$^1/_4$ cup (30g) **flaxseed meal**

$^1/_4$ cup (28g) plain pea **protein powder**

$^3/_4$ cup (185g) canned **diced tomatoes**

Allergen-Free Options

nut-free: replace the walnuts with $^1/_3$ cup (47g) sunflower seeds.

coconut-free: replace the coconut milk with a very low-carb plant-based cooking cream. Ⓜ will vary

soy-free (but higher carb): replace the soybeans with a 15-ounce (425g) can of black beans, drained (about $1^1/_2$ cups [258g]).
Ⓜ 8.1g PRO | 12g FAT | 7.2g NC

Note: macro notes are per serving and are only provided when and where the difference from the original recipe macros exceeds 10%.

Directions

-1- Prepare the onion, garlic, and ginger root as per the ingredient list.

-2- In a medium-sized sauté pan, heat the oil on medium-low heat. When hot, add the onion, garlic, and ginger. Cook for 4 to 5 minutes, or until onions are soft but not brown.

-3- Add the beans, pumpkin purée, coconut milk, tomato paste, tamari, nutritional yeast, spices, and salt to the pan. Using a large silicone spatula or mixing spoon, combine. Turn the temperature down to low, cover with a well-fitted lid, and heat until warmed through, about 5 to 7 minutes.

-4- Meanwhile, chop the walnuts. Then, in a small mixing bowl, combine the nuts with the hemp hearts, flaxseed meal, and protein powder.

-5- With a potato masher or similar utensil, roughly mash the mixture in the pan. The mixture should remain somewhat chunky with some beans still whole. Don't overmash or the patties will not hold together properly.

-6- Preheat the oven to 350°F (175°C).

-7- Remove the pan from the heat and stir in the canned tomatoes. Then, add the dry mixture. Mix to form a wet dough. Set the dough aside for 5 minutes to thicken.

-8- Divide the dough into 10 large dollops of about $^1/_3$ cup (90g) each. Form these into patties about $^5/_8$-inch (1.5cm) thick and place them on a parchment-lined baking sheet. The dough will be very sticky, so if you're using your hands to form the patties, oil them well.

-9- Bake the patties for 25 minutes.

-10- Enjoy the patties hot from the oven as is, or add some additional flavor and texture by frying them on medium-low heat in some coconut oil, or oil of choice, until well browned on each side. ✎

Notes & Tips ✎

For frying, I would suggest using roughly a teaspoon of oil per patty. Each teaspoon of oil contains 4.5g fat and adds 40 calories.

Add some extra crunch and depth of flavor to the walnuts by toasting them at 350°F (175°C) for 7 to 9 minutes before using them in this recipe. If using sunflower seeds, toast these for 5 to 7 minutes.

*To make this a meal, see page 57 for some low-carb veggie side options, or check out the Tossed Salad **builder** on page 18 for guidance on constructing a low-carb side salad.*

Carb Booster Options

Add 1 cup (134g) sugar-free canned peas. Or, replace the pumpkin purée with an equal amount of unsweetened sweet potato purée. Ⓜ 5.0g NC (either option)

EGGY TOFU **salad**

YIELD 2 servings of roughly $^1/_2$ cup (128g) each, totalling 1 cup (256g)

MACROS Ⓜ (per serving) 327 calories | 9.4g protein | 31g fat | 1.0g net carbs

PREP 30 minutes, including time to press tofu | **CHILL** 30 minutes

STORE refrigerated for up to 3 days.

Ingredients

2 servings (170g) **extra-firm tofu** (equal to half of a 4-serving block or roughly 210g unpressed)

2 tablespoons (6g) chopped fresh **chives** or green onion top or 2 teaspoons dried chives

1 teaspoon chopped fresh **dill** or $^{1}/_{4}$ teaspoon dried dill

1 clove (3g) **garlic**, crushed ($^{1}/_{2}$ teaspoon)

$^{1}/_{3}$ cup (80ml/73g) vegan **mayonnaise**

2 teaspoons **nutritional yeast flakes**

$^{1}/_{8}$ teaspoon ground **black pepper**

$^{1}/_{8}$ teaspoon **kala namak**

a pinch of ground **cumin**

a pinch of **paprika**

Directions

-1- To press the tofu, place a clean dishtowel, folded in half, on the countertop. Crumble the tofu onto one half of the folded dishtowel. Don't make the crumbles too small at this point, it can be crumbled more later. Fold the unused portion of the dishtowel over the tofu. Then, place a cutting board atop the towel and 3 to 4 large heavy books atop the cutting board. Let press for about 15 minutes.

-2- Meanwhile, prepare the chives, dill, and garlic. Whisk these and the remaining ingredients together in a small mixing bowl.

-3- Remove the objects from atop the tofu. Put the pressed tofu into the mixing bowl. Crumble any large pieces into smaller crumbles during the transfer. Mix to distribute the dressing mixture throughout.

-4- Cover and refrigerate for about 30 minutes to allow the flavors to meld.

-5- Divide equally into 2 servings and enjoy cold with low-carb bread, crackers, or veggies. See some options below.

Bases to put it on/in

- Flax & Fill-in-the-Blank Bread | PAGE 28 | (1 serving - 2 slices)
  - with almond flour 224 CALS | 6.6 PRO | 18 FAT | 2.0 NC
  - with chickpea flour 196 CALS | 6.8 PRO | 12 FAT | 7.8 NC
  - with lupin flour 175 CALS | 9.4 PRO | 12 FAT | 1.3 NC
  - with peanut flour 202 CALS | 12 PRO | 13 FAT | 2.5 NC
  - with protein powder 206 CALS | 10 PRO | 15 FAT | 0.9 NC
  - with sesame flour 199 CALS | 11 PRO | 13 FAT | 3.3 NC
- Hemp & Pumpkin Seed Crackers | PAGE 30 | (2 servings - 8 crackers [64g]) 351 CALS | 21 PRO | 26 FAT | 2.6 NC
- alfalfa sprouts - $^{1}/_{2}$ cup (21g) 0.0 NC
- bell pepper, green - 1 medium (119g) 3.4 NC
- bell pepper, red - 1 medium (119g) 4.6 NC
- bell pepper, yellow - 1 medium (119g) 6.4 NC
- celery - 3 medium stalks (120g) 1.1 NC
- cucumber - $^{1}/_{3}$ medium English (100g) 2.4 NC
- lettuce, green leaf - 6 medium leaves (58g) 0.9 NC

Note: calories for the given vegetable quantities are minimal (around 5 to 30 calories) and fat is negligible. Protein is also minimal at only 0.6 to 1.2g. Base macros do not include the Eggy Tofu Salad.

Carb Booster Options

Enjoy a serving atop 2 pieces of Ryvita Multi-Grain Crispbread. 402 CALS | 12 PRO | 32 FAT | 13 NC

Notes & Tips

The weight given for tofu is pressed weight. However, most tofu comes packed in water and weighs more. By my calculation, an unpressed serving of extra-firm tofu weighs roughly 105g.

The sulfurous flavor of kala namak is what gives this dish its egginess. However, if it's not available to you, using normal salt will still create a tasty result.

The macros for crispbread may vary by country and are subject to change over time. Macros in the Carb Booster Option include the Eggy Tofu Salad.

SEASONED AIR FRYER **tofu**

YIELD 4 servings | seasoning mix: $^{1}/_{4}$ cup (23g), equal to 4 tablespoons (1 tablespoon [6g] per serving)

MACROS Ⓜ (per serving) 191 calories | 15g protein | 12g fat | 1.6g net carbs
(per tablespoon of seasoning) 21 calories | 2.4g protein | 0.3g fat | 1.2g net carbs

PREP 35 minutes | **FRY/BAKE** air fryer 10 minutes or oven 25 minutes

EQUIPMENT REQUIRED an air fryer (optional - an oven can be used)

STORE fried, seasoned but unfried, or just the marinated tofu, refrigerated, for up to 4 days.
Store the seasoning mix at room temperature for the remaining storage life of any included ingredients.

Tofu & Marinade Ingredients

6 servings (510g ✎) **extra-firm tofu** (equal to one and a half 4-serving blocks or roughly 630g unpressed)

2 tablespoons (30ml) light **olive oil** or neutral-flavored oil of choice

2 tablespoons (30ml/36g) **tamari**, soy sauce, or aminos

Seasoning Mix Ingredients

$3\frac{1}{2}$ tablespoons (18g) **nutritional yeast flakes**

$\frac{1}{2}$ teaspoon **onion powder**

$\frac{1}{2}$ teaspoon **garlic powder**

$\frac{1}{2}$ teaspoon ground **cumin**

$\frac{1}{2}$ teaspoon ground **black pepper**

$\frac{1}{8}$ teaspoon ground **cayenne pepper** (optional or to taste)

$\frac{1}{8}$ teaspoon **salt** (optional)

Veggies for sides

- asparagus - 6 medium spears (96g) Ⓜ 1.7 NC
- broccoli florets - $1\frac{1}{2}$ cups (107g) Ⓜ 4.3 NC (about 10 florets)
- Brussels sprouts - 5 sprouts (95g) Ⓜ 4.8 NC
- broccolini - 8 spears (97g) Ⓜ 1.1 NC (Tenderstem broccoli Ⓜ 2.6 NC)
- cauliflower - 1 cup chopped (107g) Ⓜ 3.1 NC
- green beans - $\frac{3}{4}$ cup chopped (90g) Ⓜ 3.7 NC (about 16 beans)
- zucchini - $\frac{1}{2}$ medium (98g) Ⓜ 2.0 NC

See page 69 for details on bell peppers, carrots, and celery. Check out the *Tossed Salad* ***builder*** on page 18 for guidance on constructing a low-carb side salad.

Note: calories for the given vegetable quantities are minimal (20 to 40 calories) and fat is negligible. Protein is 2g to 3g for all but green beans and zucchini, which have roughly 1.5g and 1g respectively. Veggie side macros do not include the Seasoned Air Fryer Tofu.

Directions

-1- To press the tofu, place a clean dishtowel, folded in half, on the countertop. Cut the tofu into roughly $\frac{3}{4}$-inch (2cm) slices. Lay these out in a single layer on one half of the dish towel. Fold the unused portion of the dishtowel over the tofu. Then, place a cutting board atop the towel and 3 to 4 large heavy books atop the cutting board. Let press for about 20 minutes.

-2- Meanwhile, whisk the seasoning mix ingredients together in one small bowl, and the oil and tamari together in another small bowl.

-3- When the tofu has finished pressing, preheat the air fryer or oven to 400°F (200°C).

-4- Cut the pressed tofu into cubes. Put the cubes in a medium-sized mixing bowl and drizzle with the oil and tamari mixture. Using a silicone spatula or mixing spoon, toss the tofu until evenly coated and marinade has been absorbed.

-5- Sprinkle the tofu with a generous layer of the seasoning mix. Gently mix to coat the tofu. Repeat until all of the seasoning mix is used up.

-6- Optionally, if desired, place your tofu cubes on wooden skewers. If using an air fryer, choose a skewer length that will fit your basket dimensions. Leave space between the cubes so all sides of the tofu can crisp.

-7- If using an air fryer, gently transfer a single layer of tofu cubes to the air fryer basket. Depending on the size/design of your air fryer, you may need to fry the tofu in batches. If using an oven, gently transfer a single layer of tofu cubes to a non-stick or parchment-lined baking sheet.

-8- Fry/bake the tofu until it has reached a desired crispiness, roughly 10 minutes in an air fryer or 25 minutes in an oven.

-9- Divide the tofu equally into 4 servings and enjoy fresh from the fryer/oven while still hot and crispy.

Notes & Tips ✎

The weight given for tofu is pressed weight. However, most tofu comes packed in water and weighs more. By my calculation, an unpressed serving of extra-firm tofu weighs roughly 105g.

Coconut Kung Pao Noodle **bowl**

Yield 3 servings

Macros Ⓜ (per serving) 261 calories | 7.1g protein | 21g fat | 7.1g net carbs

Prep 35 minutes, not including time to make Kung Pao-ish Sauce

Store refrigerated for up to 3 days.

Veggie & Noodle Ingredients

14 ounces (400g) drained **shirataki noodles** ✎ (likely 2 × 7-ounce [200g] packages)

3 heads (294g) baby **bok choy**, halved lengthwise

4 ounces (113g) **mushrooms**, halved or quartered (about 1 1/2 cups)

1 medium (61g) **carrot**, ribboned

1 1/2 teaspoons brown or black **sesame seeds**

Sauce Ingredients

1 cup (240ml) canned full-fat **coconut milk**

1/4 batch **Kung Pao-ish Sauce** | Page 66 | (approx. 1/4 cup + 2 tablespoons [90ml])

2 tablespoons (10g) **nutritional yeast flakes**

Allergen-Free Options

coconut-free: replace the coconut milk with a very low-carb plant-based cooking cream. Ⓜ will vary

soy-free: make the recipe with Kung Pao-ish Sauce made with coconut aminos. Ⓜ 6.3 PRO | 8.5 NC

Notes & Tips ✎

Shirataki noodles are not to everyone's taste, and some people find that they cause digestive upset. Preparing them properly is key and some packages lack thorough directions. I suggest using the method I've given in step 1 of the directions above.

Recipe macros are calculated with 0g net carb noodles. Some products contain net carbs. If your noodles contain net carbs, you may wish to recalculate the recipe macros to account for this.

This recipe can also be made more simply by chopping the vegetables and mushrooms and adding them to the pan with the sauce and noodles, and then simmering until desired tenderness is reached.

Without the bulk of the noodles, you will likely find the soup to be less filling than the noodle bowl.

Note: macro notes are per serving and are only provided when and where the difference from the original recipe macros exceeds 10%.

Directions

-1- Set a large pot of water to boil. Meanwhile, put the noodles into a colander and rinse them thoroughly. Boil the noodles for 2 to 3 minutes, then drain. Heat a large dry non-stick frying pan, or sauté pan, on medium heat, add the noodles. Dry fry the noodles, stirring frequently, for 3 to 4 minutes, or until dry and squeaky. I use silicone-tipped tongs for this. Remove the noodles from the heat. They can remain in the pan for later use.

-2- Prepare the bok choy, mushrooms, and carrot as per the ingredient list. ✎ Note that baby bok choy can contain a lot of dirt, so I'd suggest removing any yellowing outer leaves, slicing off any excess "butt", halving the heads lengthwise, and then leaving the pieces to soak in cold water while preparing the carrot and mushrooms. To ribbon the carrots, I use a handheld vegetable peeler.

-3- Place the vegetables and mushrooms in a large steaming basket over water. If you do not have a large steaming basket, you may need to do this in batches. Cover, bring to a boil, and steam for roughly 5 minutes, or until desired tenderness is achieved. Once cooked, remove the steaming basket from the pot to prevent overcooking.

-4- Meanwhile, whisk together the sauce ingredients in a small bowl.

-5- Return the noodles to the stovetop on medium heat and add the sauce. Bring to a low boil and cook until the sauce has thickened to a desired consistency, 4 to 7 minutes. Adjust heat as necessary and stir frequently.

-6- Divide the noodles equally between 3 dinner bowls and top with the vegetables, mushrooms, and sesame seeds (1/2 teaspoon per bowl).

Recipe Variations

Coconut Kung Pao Soup: reduce the coconut milk to 3/4 cup (180ml) and omit the sesame seeds. Thinly slice the bok choy, mushrooms, and carrot (about 1/2 cup sliced carrot). In a medium-sized saucepan, heat 1 tablespoon (15ml) sesame or preferred oil on medium heat. Add the vegetables and mushrooms and fry for 3 to 4 minutes. Add 1 3/4 cups (420ml) water, 1 tablespoon (15ml) tamari, soy sauce, or aminos, and the coconut milk, Kung Pao-ish Sauce, and nutritional yeast flakes. Bring to a simmer, cover with a well-fitted lid, and reduce the temperature to low. Simmer for 5 minutes, or until the vegetables are tender. Add 1 tablespoon (15ml) lime or lemon juice. Divide equally between 3 bowls and serve hot.

Yield roughly 3 3/4 cups (900g) or 3 bowls of 1 1/4 (300g) each

Carb Booster Options

Replace the bok choy with 3 cups (213g) broccoli florets and use 2 medium carrots (122g). Ⓜ 10 NC

Replace the shirataki noodles with 3 servings of soybean or edamame spaghetti, cooked as per package directions. Ⓜ will vary (e.g. 440 CALS | 32 PRO | 24 NC | 15 NC)

MEDITERANNEAN FAUXTTATA **bites**

YIELD 12 servings of 1 piece each, totalling 12 pieces

MACROS Ⓜ (per serving) 138 calories | 7.1g protein | 11g fat | 1.9g net carbs

PREP 20 minutes | **BAKE** 35 minutes | **COOL** 10 minutes

EQUIPMENT REQUIRED a high-powered blender and a 12-well muffin tin or 12 silicone muffin tin liners

STORE refrigerated for up to 4 days.

Filling Ingredients

$^1/_2$ cup (12g) fresh **basil leaves**, roughly chopped

$^1/_4$ cup (40g) chopped **sun-dried tomatoes** (the jarred type marinated in oil)

$^1/_4$ cup (34g) sliced black **olives**

$^1/_4$ teaspoon crushed **red pepper flakes** (optional or to taste)

Batter Ingredients

$1^1/_2$ cups (360ml) **soy** or **pea milk**

$^1/_2$ cup (80g) **pumpkin seeds**

$^1/_4$ cup (40g) **hemp hearts**

$^1/_4$ cup (20g) **nutritional yeast flakes**

3 tablespoons (21g) plain pea **protein powder**

$^1/_4$ cup (60ml/54g) light **olive oil** or neutral-flavored oil of choice

1 tablespoon (15ml) **lemon juice**

2 teaspoons **Dijon mustard**

$^1/_2$ + $^1/_4$ teaspoon **agar agar powder** ✎

$^1/_2$ teaspoon **baking powder**

1 teaspoon **Herbes de Provence** or Italian seasoning

$^1/_2$ teaspoon **kala namak** ✎

$^1/_2$ teaspoon **onion powder**

$^1/_2$ teaspoon **paprika**

$^1/_4$ teaspoon **garlic powder**

$^1/_4$ teaspoon ground **cumin**

$^1/_8$ teaspoon ground **black pepper**

Directions

-1- Preheat the oven to 350°F (175°C).

-2- Prepare the filling ingredients as per the ingredient list and put them in a medium-sized mixing bowl.

-3- Put all batter ingredients in a high-powered blender and blend to smooth.

-4- Pour the batter mixture into the mixing bowl. Using a silicone spatula or mixing spoon, mix to distribute the filling ingredients throughout.

-5- Line 12 muffin tin wells with either silicone liners or high-quality parchment paper liners.

-6- Portion the mixture out into the lined muffin tin wells. It will be a little more than $^1/_4$ cup (59g) per muffin well.

-7- Place the muffin tin in the center of the oven and bake for 35 minutes.

-8- Remove the pan from the oven, place it on a wire cooling rack, and allow the bites to cool in the pan for about 10 minutes. If cooling longer for storage, remove the bites from their wells to continue cooling on the rack.

-9- Enjoy warm.

Recipe Variations

Faux-sheesy Broccoli Bites: for the filling, use 1 cup (91g) chopped broccoli and $^1/_4$ medium (28g) onion, diced (a scant $^1/_4$ cup). Add $^1/_2$ teaspoon liquid smoke to the batter ingredients (optional). Reduce the protein powder to 2 tablespoons (14g) and increase the nutritional yeast to $^1/_2$ cup (40g). Replace the kala namak with normal salt.

Green Onion Curry Bites: for the filling, use 4 medium (60g) green onions, sliced (about 1 cup), 2 cloves (6g) garlic, crushed (1 teaspoon), 1 teaspoon grated fresh ginger, and a finely chopped Jwala chili pepper or an additional $^1/_2$ teaspoon crushed red pepper flakes (optional or to taste). For the batter ingredients, omit the mustard, herbs, cumin, onion powder, garlic powder, and paprika. Add1 teaspoon curry powder and $^1/_8$ teaspoon garam masala. M 1.5 NC

Notes & Tips ✎

Kala namak, a sulfurous black salt, is what provides an eggy flavor to the dish. It can be replaced with regular salt if unavailable to you.

These can be made without agar, but the result will be a little wetter, less eggy in texture, and more prone to sticking to parchment liners.

To make this a meal, enjoy 3 or 4 bites with a vegetable side. See page 57 for some low-carb veggie side options, or check out the TOSSED SALAD ***builder** on page 18 for guidance on constructing a low-carb side salad.*

Note: macro notes are per serving and are only provided when and where the difference from the original recipe macros exceeds 10%.

RICED EDAMAME **rolls**

YIELD 6 servings of 1 roll each, totalling 6 rolls | sauce: 6 tablespoons (90ml) (1 tablespoon [15ml] per roll)

MACROS Ⓜ (per serving) 182 calories | 7.0g protein | 14g fat | 2.7g net carbs
(per tablespoon of sauce) 66 calories | 0.2g protein | 6.9g fat | 0.7g net carbs

PREP 30 minutes

EQUIPMENT REQUIRED a small food processor (unless using pre-riced edamame or chickpea risoni)

STORE rice mixture, sauce, and prepared veggies separately, all refrigerated, for up to 3 days.
Store avocado whole or quartered to reduce browning and cut when needed.
Sesame seeds can be kept separately from wet/moist components, at room temperature, or mixed into the rice.
Store nori separately from any moist ingredients.

Rice Ingredients

1/3 cup (80ml) boiling hot **water**

3 tablespoons (30g) **chia seeds**

1 tablespoon (15ml) unsweetened **rice vinegar**

1 tablespoon (13g) granulated **allulose** or equivalent in keto-friendly sweetener of choice

1/8 teaspoon **salt**

1 1/2 cups (210g) frozen shelled **edamame**, thawed

Sauce Ingredients

1/4 cup (60ml/55g) vegan **mayonnaise**

1 tablespoon (15ml) **sriracha**

2 teaspoons **lemon juice**

1 clove (3g) **garlic**, crushed (1/2 teaspoon)

1/8 teaspoon **salt**

Filling Ingredients

2 cups (60g) baby **mixed greens** or microgreens

1 cup (43g) **alfalfa sprouts**

7 medium (56g) **radishes**, thinly sliced (about 1/2 cup or 1/2 bunch)

1 medium (136g) **avocado**, sliced into 12 long pieces

1 medium (15g) **green onion**, cut into strips

2 teaspoons brown or black **sesame seeds**

Wrappers

6 sushi **nori sheets**

Carb Booster Options

Use 2 green onions (30g total) and add one of the following options to the fillings:
1) 2 medium (122g) carrots, grated (about 1 cup),
2) 1 medium (82g) beet, grated (about 2/3 cup),
3) 1 medium (119g) red bell pepper, sliced (about 1 cup), or 4) 1/2 cup (96g) diced mango
M 1) 4.2 NC 2) 3.7 NC 3) 3.6 NC 4) 4.9 NC

Note: macro notes are per serving and are only provided when and where the difference from the original recipe macros exceeds 10%.

Directions

-1- Put the frozen edamame in a bowl with hot water. Set aside to thaw.

-2- Place the chia seeds in a small mixing bowl and whisk in the boiling hot water, vinegar, sweetener, and salt. Set aside in the fridge to gel and cool.

-3- Meanwhile, in a small bowl, whisk the sauce ingredients together. Set aside.

-4- Prepare the filling ingredients as per the ingredient list.

-5- Drain and pat dry the thawed edamame and put it and the gelled chia seed mixture in a small food processor and pulse until the edamame is rice-sized and the mixture is sticky.

-6- To construct the rolls, align a nori sheet with a shorter edge towards you. Start with the rice; you should have about 1/4 cup (58g) per roll. Spread a thin layer of the rice mixture the width of the sheet, starting from roughly 2 1/2 inches (6cm) away from the edge nearest you. There will be some space towards the far edge of the nori sheet that is not covered. Then, stack the remaining fillings atop the rice, in a horizontal line, edge to edge. I like to start with the sprouts and mixed greens. You can put the sauce inside the rolls, or use it for drizzling or dipping the finished rolls. I do a bit of each. There will be 1 tablespoon (15ml) of sauce per roll. Lastly, fold the edge nearest you over the fillings and push the hidden fillings back towards you to squish them more tightly together. Then, roll away from you to make a cylinder. Finally, use a large sharp knife to cut the roll into pieces about 1 1/4 inch (3cm) thick. Repeat until all nori sheets and filings have been used.

rice mixture

-7- Enjoy the rolls soon after constructing. The nori will start to become gummy once the moist rice mixture and fillings are added.

Recipe Variations

Double rice: double the rice ingredients and use about 1/2 cup (116g) per roll.
M 246 CALS | 12 PRO | 17 FAT | 3.8 NC

Allergen-Free Options

soy-free (but higher carb): replace the edamame with 1/2 cup (100g) chickpea risoni/rice. Cook the risoni/rice as per the package directions and refrigerate. Do this as step 1 of the recipe. For step 5, simply mix the risoni/rice and gelled chia together (no food processor needed). M 200 CALS | 9.2 NC

soy-free (lupini beans): replace the edamame with 1 1/4 cups (225g) brined lupini beans, rinsed. Omit the salt. M 7.8 PRO | 3.6 NC

Notes & Tips

You may be able to find already riced edamame in the freezer section of your supermarket. At the time of writing, Seapoint Farms made such a product.

DEVILLED CUCUMBER **slices**

YIELD 12 servings of 3 pieces each, totalling 36 pieces

MACROS Ⓜ (per serving) 90 calories | 3.1g protein | 7.6g fat | 1.2g net carbs

PREP 20 minutes, not including time to make Green Eygg Pâté

STORE topping and sliced cucumber separately, both refrigerated. Store the topping for the remaining storage life of the Green Eygg Pâté, and the sliced cucumber for up to 2 days.

Ingredients

$^{1}/_{2}$ batch (roughly 220g) **Green Eygg Pâté** | Page 74 |

$^{1}/_{3}$ cup (80ml/73g) vegan **mayonnaise**

1 tablespoon (15g) **Dijon mustard** or mustard of choice

$^{1}/_{8}$ teaspoon ground **black pepper**

a pinch of **kala namak**

1 medium (300g) English **cucumber**, cut into 36 slices

Directions

-1- In a small mixing bowl, use a fork or mini masher to fully combine the Green Eygg Pâté, mayonnaise, mustard, pepper and kala namak.

-2- Slice the cucumber and top each slice with roughly $1^{1}/_{2}$ teaspoons (i.e. $^{1}/_{2}$ tablespoon or about 8.5g) of the topping mixture. For pretty presentation, a pastry/piping bag with an open-star nozzle can be used for this. If presentation isn't important, topping can be dolloped on or put in a Ziplock bag with the corner cut off and squeezed onto the cucumber slices.

-3- Enjoy cold soon after constructing.

Recipe Variations

Devilled Eygg Dip: divide the topping mixture into 4 servings of a little over $^{1}/_{4}$ cup (roughly 75g) each. Replace the cucumber with dipping vegetables of choice. See page 69 for a list of low-carb options.

M ($^{1}/_{4}$ recipe [75g]) 258 CALS | 8.8 PRO | 23 FAT | 1.7 NC

Note: macro notes are per serving and are only provided when and where the difference from the original recipe macros exceeds 10%.

Notes & Tips ✎

Devilled egg filling often has a little bit of vinegar in it, frequently apple cider, but I didn't grow up eating it this way, so the flavor profile doesn't resonate with me. If you'd like to add vinegar, I'd suggest starting with just a teaspoon, and if that's not vinegary enough, adding another half teaspoon at a time.

This recipe is quite simple, with minimal ingredients. However, if you'd like a more flavorful topping, add any of the following options: a crushed clove of fresh garlic or some garlic powder, chopped fresh or pickled jalapeño, crushed red pepper flakes, hot sauce, or cayenne pepper, chopped chives, green onion, onion, or some onion powder, or add a seasoning blend you enjoy, such as Cajun seasoning, curry powder, or chili powder. Most of these options, in the small amounts they'd be used, won't have much impact on the overall recipe macros.

KUNG PAO-ISH **sauce**

YIELD 24 servings of roughly 1 tablespoon (15ml) each, totalling 1 1/2 cups (360ml)

MACROS Ⓜ (per serving) 27 calories | 0.5g protein | 2.3g fat | 1.0g net carbs
(per 1/6 recipe - about 1/4 cup [60ml]) 109 calories | 2.0g protein | 9.2g fat | 3.9g net carbs

PREP 20 minutes

STORE refrigerated for up to a week.

Ingredients

$^{1}/_{4}$ cup (60ml/55g) toasted **sesame oil** or peanut oil

$^{1}/_{4}$ medium (28g) **onion**, finely chopped (a scant $^{1}/_{4}$ cup)

1 tablespoon (18g) grated fresh **ginger** (about a 1-inch [2.5cm] square piece)

6 cloves (18g) **garlic**, crushed (1 tablespoon)

1 teaspoon crushed **red pepper flakes** (optional or to taste)

$^{1}/_{4}$ teaspoon ground **black pepper**

$^{1}/_{4}$ teaspoon ground **coriander** (optional)

$^{2}/_{3}$ cup (160ml) **water**

$^{1}/_{3}$ cup (80ml/95g) **tamari**, soy sauce, or aminos

2 tablespoons (30ml) unsweetened **rice vinegar** or neutral-flavored vinegar of choice

$^{1}/_{4}$ cup (50g) **allulose** or equivalent in keto-friendly sweetener of choice

1 tablespoon (8g) **cornstarch**

Directions

-1- Prepare the onion, ginger, and garlic as per the ingredient list.

-2- Heat the oil on medium-low heat in a small saucepan. When hot, add the onion, ginger, garlic, red pepper flakes, black pepper, and coriander.

-3- Fry for 3 to 4 minutes, or until onions have softened. Stir occasionally and reduce heat if necessary to prevent burning.

-4- Meanwhile, in a small bowl, whisk together roughly half of the water and the tamari, allulose, and vinegar. Add this to the saucepan, bring to a simmer, cover with a well-fitted lid, and simmer for 5 minutes.

-5- Reusing the small bowl, whisk together the remaining water and the cornstarch. Then whisk this into the saucepan. Whisk frequently while the sauce comes to a simmer and thickens. Simmer for 4 to 5 minutes, or until no longer cloudy.

-6- Enjoy in stir-fries, drizzled over proteins or bowls, or use as a dipping sauce or a soup base.

Notes & Tips ✎

This sauce is quite spicy. If you don't like spicy food, reduce or omit the crushed red pepper flakes and black pepper. It will still be a very flavorful sauce.

Cornstarch is generally a keto no-no. However, only a small amount is used here, in the grand scheme of things, and a little goes a long way. The 1 tablespoon of cornstarch in this sauce contributes about 7g net carbs in total, only 0.25g net carbs per tablespoon of sauce.

Making this sauce soy-free by using coconut aminos almost doubles the net carbs. At the time of writing, made with Coconut Secret coconut aminos, the net carbs of this sauce were 1.7g per tablespoon.

SOYBEAN **hummus**

YIELD 10 servings of roughly $^1/_4$ cup (63g) each, totalling $2^1/_2$ cups (630g)

MACROS Ⓜ (per serving) 173 calories | 7.5g protein | 15g fat | 2.8g net carbs

PREP 15 minutes, not including time to cook and cool soybeans

EQUIPMENT REQUIRED a high-powered blender

STORE refrigerated for up to 5 days.

Ingredients

1 1/2 cups (258g) cooked & cooled **soybeans**

1/2 cup (120ml) **soy** or **pea milk**

1/2 cup (120g) **tahini**

1/4 cup (60ml/54g) light **olive oil** or neutral-flavored oil of choice

1/4 cup (60ml) **lemon juice** (about 1 large lemon)

2 cloves (6g) **garlic** (1 crushed teaspoon)

1 tablespoon (5g) **nutritional yeast flakes**

1 teaspoon ground **cumin**

1 teaspoon **salt**

Veggies to dip

- bell pepper, green - 1/2 medium (60g) Ⓜ 1.7 NC
- bell pepper, red - 1/2 medium (60g) Ⓜ 2.3 NC
- bell pepper, yellow - 1/2 medium (60g) Ⓜ 3.2 NC
- carrot - 1 medium (61g) Ⓜ 4.0 NC
- celery - 2 medium stalks (80g) Ⓜ 0.7 NC
- cucumber - 1/4 medium English (75g) Ⓜ 1.8 NC
- radishes - 8 medium (64g) Ⓜ 1.1 NC
- tomatoes - 4 cherry (68g) Ⓜ 1.7 NC

Directions

-1- Put all ingredients in a high-powered blender and blend to smooth. Stop the blender occasionally to scrape down the sides if required. You may need to use a tamper to keep the mixture moving in the initial stages. If the mixture is unable to blend, add a splash of water or plant milk.

-2- Transfer the hummus to a serving bowl, or bowls, and enjoy chilled or at room temperature with low-carb vegetables, crackers, or in low-carb wraps. See some vegetable options below.

Allergen-Free Options

soy-free (lupini beans): replace the soybeans with 1 1/4 cups (225g) brined lupini beans, rinsed. Increase the milk to 3/4 cup (180ml). Reduce the salt to 1/4 teaspoon. Ⓜ 153 CALS | 5.8 PRO | 13 FAT | 3.3 NC ✎

soy-free (but higher carb): replace the soybeans with a 15-ounce (425g) can of chickpeas, drained (about 1 1/2 cups [246g]) and mix (or blend) in 1/4 cup (28g) plain pea protein powder after having blended the other ingredients to smooth. Ⓜ 13g FAT | 7.0g NC

Notes & Tips ✎

Net carbs for this recipe and its variations have the potential to be much lower. Tahini can vary greatly in carb content with 0g net carb options available. Nutritional data for Cento brand lupini beans is used in the lupini variation of this hummus. However, there are brands with much lower net carbs (and higher protein). Examples are those produced by Unico (in Canada - 1g net carb per half cup) and Brami (in the US - 0g net carbs). Conversely, there are also lupini beans with labels that show much higher net carbs, so watch out for these.

Those allergic to peanuts may also have an allergy to lupini beans. Exercise caution if you have such an allergy.

Notes: macro notes are per serving and are only provided when and where the difference from the original recipe macros exceeds 10%. For the dipping veggies, calories for the given quantities are minimal (10 to 25 calories) and fat is negligible. Protein is also minimal, about 0.5 grams only. Veggie to dip macros do not include the Soybean Hummus.

Garlic Oregano **vinaigrette**

Yield 12 servings of 1 tablespoon (15ml) each, totalling 3/4 cup (180ml)

Macros Ⓜ (per serving)
83 calories | 0.1g protein | 9.0g fat | 0.3g net carbs

Prep 10 minutes | **Rest** 1 hour (optional)

Store refrigerated for up to 2 weeks.

MCT Ranch **dressing**

Yield 10 servings of 1 tablespoon (15ml) each, totalling 1/2 cup + 2 tablespoons (150ml)

Macros Ⓜ (per serving)
46 calories | 0.5g protein | 4.5g fat | 0.5g net carbs

Prep 10 minutes | **Rest** 1 hour (optional)

Store refrigerated for up to a week.

Garlic Oregano Vinaigrette Ingredients

$^{1}/_{2}$ cup (120ml/108g) light **olive oil** or neutral-flavored oil of choice

$^{1}/_{4}$ cup (60ml) red or white **wine vinegar**

1 teaspoon **Dijon mustard**

3 cloves (9g) **garlic**, crushed (1$^{1}/_{2}$ teaspoons)

1$^{1}/_{2}$ teaspoons **allulose** or equivalent in keto-friendly sweetener of choice

1$^{1}/_{2}$ teaspoons dried **oregano**

$^{1}/_{4}$ + $^{1}/_{8}$ teaspoon **salt**

$^{1}/_{8}$ teaspoon ground **black pepper**

Garlic Oregano Vinaigrette Directions

-1- Put all ingredients in a sealed jar or container and shake to combine. Or, whisk the ingredients together in a small bowl.

-2- Refrigerate the dressing for about an hour to allow flavors to meld.

-3- Enjoy drizzled over salad ingredients of choice.

Notes & Tips

Many vinegars are essentially carb-free, but watch out for the sweet ones like balsamic. Unfortunately, these can be shockingly high in carbs.

MCT Ranch Dressing Ingredients

$^{1}/_{3}$ cup (80ml) **soy** or **pea milk**

2 scoops (20g) vegan **MCT oil powder** (see coconut-free option if this is not available to you)

2 teaspoons **lemon juice**

1 teaspoon **apple cider vinegar** or neutral-flavored vinegar of choice

a few drops of vegan **Worcestershire sauce** (optional)

1 clove **garlic**, crushed ($^{1}/_{2}$ teaspoon)

1 teaspoon **nutritional yeast flakes**

1 teaspoon dried **parsley**

$^{1}/_{2}$ teaspoon dried **dill**

$^{1}/_{2}$ teaspoon **onion powder**

$^{1}/_{4}$ teaspoon **garlic powder**

$^{1}/_{4}$ teaspoon ground **black pepper**

$^{1}/_{4}$ teaspoon **salt**

3 tablespoons (45ml) vegan **mayonnaise**

See the Tossed Salad **builder** on page 18 for guidance on constructing a low-carb salad on which to use these dressings.

MCT Ranch Dressing Directions

-1- In a small bowl or jar, whisk together all ingredients apart from the mayonnaise. Then, gently whisk in the mayonnaise.

-2- Refrigerate the dressing for about an hour to allow flavors to meld.

-3- Enjoy drizzled or dolloped over salad ingredients of choice.

Recipe Variations

MCT Ranch Dip: whisk an additional 3 scoops (30g) MCT oil powder into the dressing to further thicken it. This will bring the yield to roughly $^{3}/_{4}$ cup (195g), or 3 servings of $^{1}/_{4}$ cup (65g) each. See page 69 for some dipping vegetable options. M 212 CALS | 1.6 PRO | 21 FAT | 1.5 NC

Allergen-Free Options

coconut-free: omit the MCT oil powder and increase the mayonnaise to $^{1}/_{4}$ cup (60ml/55g). This change will result in a thinner dressing. To thicken, you could add $^{1}/_{16}$ teaspoon (half of $^{1}/_{8}$ teaspoon) xanthan gum. Mix the xanthan gum with the nutritional yeast, herbs, and spices and then whisking this mixture into the milk. Allow 10 to 15 minutes for the dressing to thicken fully. For a coconut-free dip, increase the mayonnaise to $^{1}/_{4}$ cup + 2 tablespoons (90ml/83g) and thicken with $^{1}/_{8}$ teaspoon xanthan gum in the same manner as suggested above.

Notes & Tips

MCT oil powder often contains acacia fiber. A product without acacia fiber, or a similar fiber agent, might not have the thickening effect of one that does.

Note: macro notes are per serving and are only provided when and where the difference from the original recipe macros exceeds 10%.

BACONY **bits**

YIELD
pea-based TVP: 16 servings of roughly 1 tablespoon (5g) each, totalling 1 cup (80g)
soy-based TVP: 16 servings of roughly 2 teaspoons (5g) each, totalling 1/2 cup + 2 tablespoons (80g)

MACROS (per serving)
pea-based TVP: 29 calories | 2.6g protein | 1.9g fat | 0.2g net carbs
soy-based TVP: 27 calories | 1.8g protein | 1.7g fat | 0.7g net carbs

PREP 10 minutes | **BAKE** 30 to 40 minutes | **COOL** 5 minutes

STORE completely dehydrated and fully cooled, at room temperature, for up to a month.

Ingredients

1 cup (160g) **pumpkin seeds**

1 cup (240ml) **water**

1 1/2 teaspoons **agar agar powder**

1/4 cup (20g) **nutritional yeast flakes**

1/2 teaspoon **kala namak** ✎

1/2 teaspoon **onion powder**

1/4 teaspoon **garlic powder**

Directions

-1- Put the pumpkin seeds in a medium-sized saucepan, add water until there is at least 2 inches (5cm) of water above the seeds, bring to a boil on high heat, and boil for 15 minutes. Monitor and add water if necessary.

-2- Once boiled, using a colander or metal sieve, drain and rinse the seeds. Then, put the seeds into the carafe of a high-powered heat-safe blender.

-3- In a small saucepan, whisk together the water and agar agar powder. Bring to a boil on medium heat, reduce to low, and simmer for 3 to 4 minutes. Whisk frequently.

-4- Meanwhile, add the remaining ingredients to the blender.

-5- Add the agar agar and water mixture to the blender and blend to smooth. You may need to stop occasionally and scrape down the sides to make sure all bits are getting fully blended. The mixture will be very hot. Be careful.

-6- Prepare a container, or containers, in which to set your pâté. You'll have about 2 cups (480ml) of mixture to set, so select accordingly. Some good options are a shallow rectangular or square glass storage container or a silicone loaf pan. Or, for single servings, 8 silicone muffin wells. If using single-serving wells, you'll use roughly 1/4 cup (55g) per well. You may wish to use oil or parchment paper with non-silicone items to prevent sticking and facilitate easy removal.

-7- Put the blended mixture in your chosen vessel(s), smooth out the top(s), and allow the pâté to cool at room temperature for about half an hour. Then, transfer it to the fridge to set for another 3 1/2 hours, or until fully chilled.

-8- Slice or cube and enjoy cold or at room temperature with low-carb vegetables or crackers. See page 55 for some options.

Recipe Variations

Sheesy Jalapeño Pâté:

Replace the kala namak with regular salt, increase the nutritional yeast to 1/2 cup (40g), and add:

1/2 cup (70g) canned/jarred **jalapeño slices**

1 1/2 tablespoons (23ml) **lemon juice** (about 1/2 medium lemon)

1 tablespoon (18g) white or chickpea **miso**

1/2 teaspoon ground **cumin**

Chop roughly half of the jalapeño slices into small pieces. Put the other half in the blender along with the other ingredients (those listed here and in the original ingredient list). After blending to smooth, stir in the jalapeño pieces.

Yield 8 servings of roughly 70g each, totalling 560g

Ⓜ 147 CALS | 10 PRO | 2.6 NC

Shiitake Herb Pâté: see page 81

Note: macro notes are per serving and are only provided when and where the difference from the original recipe macros exceeds 10%.

Notes & Tips ✎

Kala namak, a sulfurous black salt, is what provides the eggy flavor in this recipe. However, feel free to use normal salt if kala namak isn't available to you. The result won't be as eggy, but will still be tasty, nutritious, and protein-rich.

Do not use a bullet blender for this recipe. At best, you'll have a very hard time removing the base. At worst, the hot contents will explode all over you.

This pâté is on the firmer side to allow it to be sliced. If you'd prefer it to be more spreadable, you could reduce the amount of agar agar powder.

SOFT INSTANT POT soybeans

YIELD roughly $9^1/_2$ cups (1,650g)

MACROS Ⓜ (per $^1/_2$ cup [86g] cooked beans)
148 calories | 16g protein | 7.7g fat | 1.8g net carbs

PREP 5 minutes | **COOK** 1 hour 15 minutes

EQUIPMENT REQUIRED an Instant Pot or pressure cooker of choice

STORE refrigerated for up to 5 days,
or freeze in user-friendly portions.

CAULIFLOWER rice

YIELD roughly 5 cups (650g)

MACROS Ⓜ (per 1 cup [130g] cooked rice)
30 calories | 2.4g protein | 0.6g fat | 2.3g net carbs

PREP 20 minutes (or more if grating cauliflower by hand)

EQUIPMENT REQUIRED a chute-style food processor with a large grating blade or a large handheld box grater

STORE refrigerated for up to 4 days,
or freeze in user-friendly portions.

Soft Instant Pot Soybeans Ingredients

4 cups (712g) dry **soybeans**

roughly 10 cups (2.5L) **water**

Soft Instant Pot Soybeans Directions

-1- Rinse the soybeans and remove any debris or funny-looking beans.

-2- Put the beans in your Instant Pot and fill with water until there is about $1^1/_2$ to 2 inches (4 to 5cm) of water above the soybeans.

-3- Lock the lid and make sure the pressure valve is sealed. Pressure cook on high pressure for 50 minutes. ✎

-4- Allow the pot to depressurize naturally for 15 minutes before releasing the pressure manually. Unlock the lid.

-5- Drain away excess liquid, rinse the beans, and enjoy in your favorite dishes.

Notes & Tips ✎

If you prefer to soak your beans overnight, feel free. Reduce the cooking time to 30 minutes for soaked beans.

Soybean cooking times can vary vastly by product. I have found that to get soft beans, I have to cook them much longer than some recipes I've seen online. There are recipes that suggest cooking times as low as 10 minutes for soaked beans or 15 minutes for unsoaked ones, which I find unimaginable. I have purchased beans that took even longer than 50 minutes in the Instant Pot to soften thoroughly.

I have had little success cooking soybeans to soft on the stovetop. After overnight soaking and hours of simmering, they have always remained quite a lot firmer than I like. An Instant Pot works miracles on soybeans in comparison.

Canned or jarred soybeans are available, but not that easy to find in most stores. Eden and Biona are brands you can look for. Labels on both of these products boast substantially higher carbs than the national nutritional database information for soybeans cooked from dried.

Cauliflower Rice Ingredients

1 medium-large (675g) trimmed head **cauliflower**

roughly $^1/_4$ cup (60ml) **water**

Cauliflower Rice Directions

-1- Break the head of cauliflower into large florets, either of a size that will fit through the chute of your food processor, or that you can comfortably hold in your hand if using a box grater.

-2- Grate the cauliflower and put it in a medium-sized microwave-safe bowl.

-3- Add the water to the bowl and cover with a microwave-safe plate or lid.

-4- Microwave for 5 minutes. Carefully remove the bowl from the microwave and mix. Be very cautious here as the bowl will be full of hot steam.

-5- Return the rice to the microwave and steam it for another 3 minutes before mixing again and checking if it's cooked. Cooked rice will be tender, but not mushy, and will have a somewhat translucent appearance. If not cooked, return it to the microwave and cook it in 2-minute increments until done.

-6- Enjoy hot or cold as a side dish, a base for various bowls, or in salads.

Notes & Tips ✎

There are many ways to turn a head of cauliflower into rice. This is my preferred method, as I find it makes for consistently-sized and evenly -cooked results. If this recipe is too equipment-laden for your kitchen, a quick Google search will give you other methods of preparation that may better suit you. Various storebought cauliflower rice options are also available, though I haven't found any I especially like.

PUMPKIN **spice** & CHILI **powder**

YIELD 24 servings of 1 teaspoon (≈2g) each, totalling 8 tablespoons or 1/2 cup (≈55g)

MACROS Ⓜ (per serving)
Pumpkin Spice: 7 calories | 0.1g protein | 0.1g fat | 0.8g net carbs
Chili Powder: 7 calories | 0.3g protein | 0.2g fat | 0.8g net carbs

PREP 10 minutes

STORE at room temperature for the remaining storage life of any included ingredients.

Pumpkin Spice Ingredients

$^1/_4$ cup + 1 tablespoon (39g) ground **cinnamon**

$1^1/_2$ tablespoons (8g) ground **ginger**

$1^1/_2$ teaspoons ground **cloves**

$1^1/_2$ teaspoons ground **allspice**

$1^1/_2$ teaspoons ground **nutmeg**

Pumpkin Spice Directions

-1- Put all ingredients in a spice jar or sealable vessel of choice and shake to combine.

-2- Add to recipes and dishes as needed.

Chili Powder Ingredients

$^1/_4$ cup (27g) **paprika**, preferably smoked, or ancho chili powder

1 tablespoon (6g) ground **cumin**

1 tablespoon (10g) **garlic powder**

2 teaspoons **onion powder**

2 teaspoons dried **oregano**

$1^1/_2$ teaspoons **cayenne pepper** (or less)

$^1/_2$ teaspoon ground **allspice**

Chili Powder Directions

-1- Put all ingredients in a spice jar or sealable vessel of choice and shake to combine.

-2- Optionally, you may wish to briefly blend the mixture in a bullet blender to better incorporate the oregano into the mixture.

-3- Add to recipes and dishes as needed.

Notes & Tips

Traditionally chili powder is made with powdered ancho chilis, which are mild and smoky. However, this spice can be hard to come by and so I've suggested smoked paprika as the primary ingredient option. If you are using ancho chili powder and you are sensitive to spice, you may wish to reduce the amount of cayenne pepper or replace it with paprika or additional ancho chili powder.

If you have a low spice tolerance, either fully or partially replace the cayenne pepper with ancho chili powder or paprika.

To avoid any confusion, none of the pictured chilis are ancho or cayenne peppers. These peppers were not readily available to me for photographing.

FALAFEL-INSPIRED BREAKFAST **bars**

YIELD 6 servings of 1 bar each, totalling 6 bars

MACROS Ⓜ (per serving) 236 calories | 12g protein | 19g fat | 3.7g net carbs

PREP 35 minutes | **BAKE** 25 minutes | **COOL** 15 minutes

EQUIPMENT REQUIRED a 7-inch (18cm) square baking pan or a 9 by 5-inch (23 by 13cm) loaf pan

STORE at room temperature for up to 24 hours or refrigerated for up to 5 days.

WET INGREDIENTS

1/4 cup (60ml) room temperature **water**

1 tablespoon (8g) **flaxseed meal**

1 teaspoon **tamari**, soy sauce, or aminos

1/4 cup (63g) **almond butter**

1/4 cup (61g) canned **pumpkin purée**

1 1/2 tablespoons (23ml) light **olive oil** or neutral-flavored oil of choice

1/2 cup (64g) grated **carrot** (about 1 medium)

1/8 medium (14g) **onion**, diced (about 2 tablespoons)

2 tablespoons (8g) finely chopped **parsley** or 2 teaspoons dried parsley flakes

1 clove (3g) **garlic**, crushed (1/2 teaspoon)

DRY INGREDIENTS

1/2 cup (50g) **walnuts**, coarsely chopped

1/4 cup (40g) **hemp hearts**

1/3 cup (37g) plain pea **protein powder**

1 tablespoon (5g) **nutritional yeast flakes**

1/2 teaspoon **baking powder**

1/2 teaspoon ground **cumin**

1/4 teaspoon **onion powder**

1/4 teaspoon crushed **red pepper flakes** (optional or to taste)

1/8 teaspoon **garlic powder**

1/8 teaspoon ground **coriander**

1/8 teaspoon ground **cardamon**

1/8 teaspoon ground **black pepper**

1/8 teaspoon **salt**

DIRECTIONS

-1- In a medium-sized mixing bowl, whisk together the water, flaxseed meal, and tamari. Set aside to gel.

-2- Preheat the oven to 350°F (175°C).

-3- Prepare the carrot, onion, parsley, garlic, and walnuts as per the ingredient list.

-4- In a small mixing bowl, whisk together the dry ingredients.

-5- Line a 7-inch (18cm) square cake pan, or 9 by 5-inch (23 by 13cm) loaf pan, with parchment paper. Allow the parchment to hang over two sides for easy removal of the bars.

-6- Whisk the almond butter, pumpkin purée, and oil into the flax mixture.

-7- Add the veggies/herbs and the dry mixture to the wet mixture. Using a silicone spatula or mixing spoon, mix until a soft dough has formed and no dry patches remain.

-8- Transfer the dough to the lined pan. Using oiled hands or a clean silicone spatula, gently press the dough into an even layer.

-9- Place the pan in the center of the oven and bake for 25 minutes, or until the edges are golden brown.

-10- Remove the bars from the oven and allow them to cool in the pan for 5 minutes. Then, gently transfer the bars from the pan to a wire cooling rack to cool for an additional 10 minutes.

-11- Cut into 6 bars. Enjoy warm or at room temperature.

CARB BOOSTER OPTIONS

Increase the water to 1/2 cup (120ml) and add 1/4 cup (28g) rolled oats alongside the flaxseed meal. Reduce the almond butter to 3 tablespoons (47g). Ⓜ 6.1 NC

ALLERGEN-FREE OPTIONS *See page 22 for allergen-free options.*

NOTES & TIPS *See page 22 for recipe notes.*

Note: macro notes are per serving and are only provided when and where the difference from the original recipe macros exceeds 10%.

SHIITAKE HERB **pâté**

YIELD 6 servings of roughly 75g each, totalling 450g

MACROS Ⓜ (per serving) 135 calories | 7.2g protein | 9.6g fat | 2.7g net carbs

PREP 30 minutes | **SET** about 4 hours

EQUIPMENT REQUIRED a high-powered heat-safe blender ✎

STORE refrigerated up to 5 days. Pâte can also be frozen with minimal impact on texture.

BASE INGREDIENTS

$^1/_2$ cup (80g) **pumpkin seeds**

$^3/_4$ cup (180ml) **water**

1 teaspoon **agar agar powder**

$^1/_4$ cup (20g) **nutritional yeast flakes**

$^1/_2$ teaspoon **salt**

$^1/_2$ teaspoon **onion powder**

$^1/_4$ teaspoon **garlic powder**

MUSHROOM MIXTURE INGREDIENTS

1$^1/_2$ tablespoons (23ml) light **olive oil** or neutral-flavored oil of choice

4 ounces (113g) **shiitake mushrooms**, sliced (about 2 cups)

$^1/_4$ medium (28g) **onion**, diced (a scant $^1/_4$ cup)

1 clove (3g) **garlic**, crushed ($^1/_2$ teaspoon)

1$^1/_2$ teaspoons **Herbes de Provence** or Italian seasoning

$^1/_8$ teaspoon crushed **red pepper flakes** (optional)

1$^1/_2$ teaspoons **tamari**, soy sauce, or aminos

NOTES & TIPS ✎

This pâté is on the firmer side to allow it to be sliced. If you'd like it to be more spreadable, you could reduce the amount of agar agar powder.

Do not use a bullet blender for this recipe. At best, you'll have a very hard time removing the base. At worst, the hot contents will explode all over you.

DIRECTIONS

-1- Put the pumpkin seeds in a medium-sized saucepan, add water until there is at least 2 inches (5cm) of water above the seeds, bring to a boil on high heat, and boil for 15 minutes. Monitor and add water if necessary.

-2- Once boiled, using a colander or metal sieve, drain and rinse the seeds, and then put them into the carafe of a high-powered heat-safe blender.

-3- Meanwhile, prepare the mushrooms, onion, and garlic as per the ingredient list.

-4- In a medium-sized frying pan, heat the oil on medium-low heat. When hot, add the garlic, onion, herbs, and red pepper flakes to the pan. Cook for 4 to 5 minutes, or until onions are soft but not brown. Add the mushrooms and drizzle with the tamari. Increase the heat to medium and sauté for another 5 to 7 minutes, or until mushrooms are tender. Stir frequently. When cooked, add the mixture to the blender.

-5- Meanwhile, put the nutritional yeast, salt, onion powder, and garlic powder in the blender.

-6- In a small saucepan, whisk together the water and agar agar powder. Bring to a boil on medium heat, reduce to low, and simmer for 3 to 4 minutes. Whisk frequently.

-7- Add the agar agar and water mixture to the blender and blend to smooth. You may need to stop occasionally and scrape down the sides to make sure all bits are getting fully blended. The mixture will be very hot. Be careful.

-8- Prepare a container, or containers, in which to set your pâté. You'll have about 2 cups (480ml) of mixture to set, so select accordingly. Some good options are a shallow rectangular or square glass storage container or a silicone loaf pan. Or, for single servings, 6 silicone muffin wells. If using single-serving wells, you'll use roughly $^1/_3$ cup (75g) per well. You may wish to use oil or parchment paper with non-silicone items to prevent sticking and facilitate easy removal.

-9- Put the blended mixture in your chosen vessel(s), smooth out the top(s), and cool at room temperature for about half an hour. Then, transfer the pâte to the fridge to set for another 3$^1/_2$ hours, or until fully chilled.

-10- Slice or cube and enjoy cold or at room temperature with low-carb vegetables or crackers. See page 55 for some options.

The 5-week **meal plan**

Overview

This book comes with soy-inclusive and soy-free meal plans. The former can be found on the following pages, while the latter can be download from keto4vegans.com/resources. Nutrition-wise, both plans broadly cater to the needs of a lightly active woman aiming to maintain her weight. However, these plans can, and should, be adjusted to suit your individual needs and objectives.

Throughout the plan, the day-to-day calories and macronutrient grams vary somewhat. However, the average daily macros for these meal plans are as follows:

soy-inclusive: 1,668 calories | 79g protein | 127g fat | 27g net carbs
soy-free: 1,631 calories | 74g protein | 122g fat | 32g net carbs

Adjusting the macros

Whether you're following the soy-inclusive or the soy-free meal plan, the calorie and macronutrient intake should be adjusted, broadly, to meet your individual goals and nutritional requirements. If you're not sure what your requirements are, see "Finding and tracking your macros" on page 7 for guidance. Simple adjustments to the meal plan can be made with relative ease.

Protein: a higher protein intake may be helpful, or necessary, for those trying to lose weight, gain muscle, or prevent age-related muscle loss. Daily protein intake can easily be increased by adding a scoop of protein powder, another glass of soy/pea milk, some additional soybeans or lupini beans, or an extra serving of tofu to your meals. These low-fat options are relatively low in both calories and net carbs. Adding nuts and seeds, especially protein-rich hemp and pumpkin seeds, is a higher-fat, and thus higher-calorie option. Nuts and seeds may also be a higher-carb option, depending on your selection. Nutritional details for some protein boosting options can be found in the "Nut & seed toppings" section of page 21 and the "Protein-rich toppings or sides" section of page 37.

Fat & calories: active women, men, and those who are above-average height, or in larger bodies, may find they require more fat and calories than the meal plan provides. Higher fat intake can be achieved via whole foods or with added oils. Macadamia nuts, pecans, and avocados are especially high in fat and low in net carbs. Nutritional details for these nuts can be found on page 21. A medium avocado (136g) contains 227 calories and 2.4g net carbs.

To increase fat/calorie intake without adding any carbs, additional oil can be added to salad dressings or during cooking, and MCT oil powder can be whisked into plant milk, chia pudding, coffees or teas, or blended into smoothies and frappés. A 10-gram scoop of MCT oil powder typically has 60 calories, while a teaspoon (5ml) of oil has 40 calories and a tablespoon (15ml) has 119 calories.

Higher-carb: To increase carbs, small amounts of higher-carb foods can be added to meals (e.g. starchy vegetables, fruit, or grains), or larger quantities of low-carb vegetables can be added. Nutritional details for some fruit options can be found in the "Fruit toppings" section of page 21 and some low-carb vegetable options can be found in the "Veggie sides" section of page 57 and the "Veggies to dip" section of page 69. There is also the Tossed Salad **builder** on page 18. The simple salads that appear throughout the plan could be replaced with more diverse and carb-rich ones. In addition, many recipes in the book include "Carb Booster Options". These could also be utilized to increase the carbs in the meal plan.

Lower-carb: On some days, carbs can easily be reduced by omitting the berries, or by replacing red pepper sticks with green pepper sticks or radishes. On other days, adjustment would need to be made to the recipes themselves in order to reduce the carbs, which is a more involved task. Note that omitting the simple salads and avocados would have only a small impact on the daily carbs, but a larger impact on the fat/calories, and on vitamin and mineral intake.

Lower-calorie: Adding to a meal plan is far easier than subtracting from one, and so, I have created lower-calorie versions of both the soy-inclusive and soy-free meal plans. For the most part, these plans halve breakfast, reducing the calories to an average of about 1,450 per day. To maintain roughly a 70g protein intake, these plans include additional daily soy/pea milk or protein powder. With breakfast halved, the lower-calorie plans are also slightly lower in net carbs. These plans can be downloaded from the website.

Those who have a high protein requirement, but a relatively low calorie requirement may find that using one of the lower-calorie meal plans, and adding the necessary additional protein to it, is a better option than trying to adapt one of the original plans.

Organization & preparation

Each day of the meal plan is organised into 3 main meals: breakfast, lunch, and dinner. However, feel free to rearrange meals and meal components to suit your habits and schedule. For those used to snacking, items such as bars, bread, crackers, simple salads, avocados, and veggie sticks can easily be enjoyed between meals. Those accustomed to eating something sweet after dinner can set aside a portion of a breakfast bar, a dollop of chia pudding, or some berries for this purpose. Those who work in the evenings, when new meals are typically prepared, can make and enjoy the dinner recipes for lunch, and instead take the lunch items to work for dinner. The plan is flexible. Make the changes that accommodate your needs.

In addition to the 3 main meals, there are two additional items included in every day of the meal plan: an 8-ounce (240ml) glass of soy or pea milk, for protein and the micronutrients plant milks are typically fortified with, and a packet of seaweed snacks, for iodine. These items can be enjoyed at whatever time of day best suits you. If soy or pea milk is not available or palatable to you, another type of low-carb plant milk with a half scoop, or 2 tablespoons (14g), of protein powder can be substituted in its place. Seaweed snacks can be omitted with little impact on macros, and iodized salt or a supplement can be used to meet iodine needs. In addition to the milk and seaweed snacks, there are a couple of other low-carb items that, at your discretion, could be added to each day: a serving of sauerkraut, for probiotics, and sugar-free dill pickles and/or low/no-carb bouillon cubes or vegetable broth, for added sodium. Including these items should have minimal impact on daily macros.

The preparation of new meals typically takes place in the evening, for dinner, with leftovers being available for future lunches and dinners. Breakfast items, and occasional lunch items may need to be prepared the evening before if you work a typical nine-to-five type schedule and do not wish to wake up early and bake. Certain items have particularly long preparation, baking, or cooling times (◷) or should be made, in-part or entirely, well in advance (⚘) of when they are to be eaten. This will need to be taken into account when planning your day/week. Thus, it's wise to check the preparation details of upcoming recipes at least a day in advance.

When a new recipe needs to be made, it will appear in bold and be accompanied by the page on which to find the recipe. Non-bolded recipe names refer to leftover servings. Non-recipe meal items (e.g. mixed greens or buttery spread) are also not in bold. Occasionally, recipes should be made as half batches (◐) or double batches (◎). This will be noted directly after the recipe page number.

For efficient use of ingredients, to reduce time spent in the kitchen, and to lend variety to the meal plan, you may be instructed to freeze (❄) servings of recipes or recipe ingredients for future use. Instructions will also be provided to later thaw (❄>) these items. Be sure to take items out to thaw well prior to when they are needed.

Unless indicated otherwise, you are to consume a single serving of the recipe. If you're meant to consume more than a single serving, this will be noted. For example, (×2) indicates that you are to eat 2 servings of that recipe. A single serving of salad dressing or Bacony Bits is one tablespoon. For reference, a tablespoon is 15ml. Non-recipe items that accompany meals are given in portions of the food (e.g. $^1/_2$ medium red bell pepper) as well as in grams. The weight measurements are for the edible components only.

For the majority of recipes, you will be eating all servings of the recipe at some point during the meal plan. If servings will not be used, this will be noted so you can act accordingly. If you wish to share your tasty creations with others, feel free, and simply anticipate making the recipe again at a future point in time in order to have enough servings for yourself. If sharing and remaking recipes, keep in mind that the shopping lists only account for making the recipe as many times as the meal plan suggests, so you will have to anticipate making adjustments there as well.

ALLERGIES & SUBSTITUTIONS

Recipes that contain common allergens almost always include an "ALLERGEN-FREE OPTIONS" section. Coconut-free, peanut-free, and nut-free options are nutritionally similar to the original recipe and can be made use of in the meal plan without significantly impacting the daily macros. However, these changes will require some small adjustments to the non-perishable shopping list. To make the meal plan coconut-free, use the INGREDIENT SWAPS options for coconut oil and MCT oil powder given on page 85, and replace the cans of coconut milk with an equivalent amount of very low-carb plant-based cooking cream. To make the plan peanut-free, replace the peanuts with either 2.3oz (65g) silvered almonds or 2.8oz (80g) pumpkin seeds (these can be toasted). To make the plan nut-free, omit the almond extract, replace the almond butter with an equal amount of sunflower seed butter, and replace the Brazil nuts, peanuts, and walnuts with 15oz (428g) sunflower seeds, 7.1oz (200g) pumpkin seeds, and 0.7oz (20g) hemp hearts.

DOWNLOADS & SUPPORT

The soy-inclusive meal plan included in this book's pages, along with these notes and the shopping lists, can be downloaded at keto4vegans.com/resources. The soy-free and lower-calorie meal plans, with notes and shopping lists, are available at the same location.

For support, join me, and others, in the Keto4Vegans Facebook community. Until then, I wish you happy and healthy eating!

THE SHOPPING LIST: non-perishable items

The shopping lists are divided into 2 categories: non-perishable items and perishable items. To reduce overall shopping time, the quantities given in non-perishable list are for the entire meal plan. If you prefer more traditional weekly shopping lists, these can be downloaded from keto4vegans.com/resources. The below version of the shopping list is available at the same location.

Cans of coconut milk, pumpkin purée, chopped tomatoes, and tomato sauce will be used in their entirety. Stored properly, once opened, these items should keep for up to a week. If they aren't being used within that period, there will be notes in the meal plan instructing you to freeze portions for future use. Whether or not you need to freeze tomato paste, and how much will be left over, will depend on how your product is packaged; package types and sizes vary a great deal country to country.

Required amounts of dried herbs and spices are not provided as the weights are frequently negligible. As a rule of thumb, if you expect to soon run out of a particular herb or spice on the list, I'd suggest buying another bottle/pouch next time you go shopping.

Note that ounce quantities are rounded to whole numbers once double digits are reached (e.g. 19.3 will be rounded down to 19).

check that it's vegan · beware of high-carb products · see notes · optional item · ingredient swap available

CANNED OR JARRED ITEMS

- **almond butter**, unsweetened, smooth - 19oz (547g)
- **coconut milk**, full-fat, 13.5floz (400ml) cans - 4 cans
- **jalapeño pepper slices**, pickled - 2.5oz (70g)
- **lupini beans**, brined - 1.6oz (45g)
- **olives**, black, sliced - 4.8oz (135g)
- **pumpkin purée**, unsweetened, 15oz (425g) cans - 2 cans
- **tahini** - 4.2oz (120g)
- **tomatoes, chopped** - 14.5oz (411g) cans - 2 cans (fire-roasted with garlic is a nice option if available)
- **tomato sauce** - 15oz (425g) cans - 1 can
- **tomato paste** - 2.9oz (82g)
- **tomatoes**, sun-dried, marinated in oil - 2.8oz (80g)

CONDIMENTS, SAUCES & OILS

- **liquid smoke** - 0.4floz (13ml)
- **mayonnaise** - 14floz (424ml)
- **mustard**, Dijon - 2.6oz (73g)
- **oil, coconut** - 9.8floz (290ml)
- **oil, olive**, light or neutral-flavored - 32floz (949ml)
- **oil, sesame** (toasted) - 2.0floz (60ml)
- **sriracha** - 1.1oz (31g/25ml)
- **tamari**, **soy sauce**, or **aminos** - 5.8floz (172ml)
- **vinegar, apple cider** - 1.9floz (55ml)

CONDIMENTS, SAUCES & OILS continued

- **vinegar, red** or **white wine/grape** - 3.0floz (90ml)
- **vinegar, rice**, unsweetened - 1.5floz (45ml)
- **Worcestershire sauce** - 0.1floz (2.5ml)

NUTS & SEEDS

- **Brazil nuts** - 2.0oz (58g)
- **chia seeds** - 23oz (646g)
- **hemp hearts** - 36oz (1,007g)
- **peanuts**, oil-roasted, salted - 2.5oz (72g)
- **pumpkin seeds**, shelled - 22oz (613g)
- **sesame seeds**, brown or black - 2.9oz (83g)
- **walnuts**, whole - 18oz (500g)

BAKING INGREDIENTS

- **agar agar powder** - 0.2oz (4.5g)
- **allulose** or sweetener of choice, granulated (e.g. erythritol or an erythritol blend) - 25oz (707g)
- **almond extract**, alcohol or oil-based, sugar-free - 0.5floz (15ml)
- **baking powder** - 1.8oz (52g)
- **chocolate chips**, vegan (i.e. dark), keto-friendly - 3.2oz (90g)
- **cocoa/cacao powder**, unsweetened - 2.3oz (65g)
- **cornstarch** - 0.3oz (8g)
- **flaxseed meal**, preferably golden - 8.5oz (240g)

Baking Ingredients continued

- **stevia**, liquid, preferably maple-flavored - a few drops
- **lupin flour** - 4.8oz (135g)
- **psyllium husks**, whole - 2.9oz (83g)
- **salt** - 2.1oz (59g)
- **vanilla extract**, alcohol-based, sugar-free - 2.3floz (68ml)
- **xanthan gum** - 0.2oz (4.8g)

Miscellaneous

- **bouillon cubes**, vegetable - 3 cubes
- **edamame**, shelled, frozen - 7.4oz (210g)
- **nori sheets**, the kind used to roll sushi - 6 sheets
- **MCT oil powder** - 2.5oz (70g)
- **nutritional yeast flakes** - 7.6oz (214g)
- **parchment paper** - a roll
- **parchment muffin liners** - 24 liners
- **protein powder, plain**, preferably pea - 6.6oz (186g)
- **protein powder, vanilla-flavored** - 11oz (298g)
- **seaweed snacks**, salted - 35 x 0.17oz (5g) packets
- **shirataki/konjac noodles** - 14oz (400g)
- **soybeans**, dry - 25oz (700g)
- **teabags, berry-flavored** - 2 teabags
- **TVP**, preferably pea-based - 4.8oz (135g) (e.g. Plant Boss Meatless Crumbles - 1 1/2 bags)

Dried Herbs & Spices

- **bay leaf**, whole
- **black pepper**, ground
- **cardamon**, ground
- **cayenne pepper**
- **chili powder**
- **cinnamon**, ground
- **coriander**, ground
- crushed **red pepper flakes**
- **cumin**, ground
- **curry powder**
- **dill**, dried
- **garam masala**
- **garlic powder**
- **Herbes de Provence**
- **kala namak**
- **nutmeg**, ground
- **onion powder**
- **oregano**, dried
- **paprika**, smoked if available
- **parsley**, dried
- **pumpkin spice**
- **thyme**, dried

Ingredient Swaps

lupini beans ⇄ pumpkin seeds [1.1oz (30g)]

coconut oil ⇄ neutral-flavored oil of choice (e.g. light olive oil)

apple cider vinegar and rice vinegar ⇄ red or white wine/grape vinegar

chocolate chips ⇄ very dark low-sugar chocolate (e.g. Lindt 90%)

lupin flour ⇄ flaxseed meal [2.4oz (68g)] and plain pea protein powder [2.2oz (63g)]

xanthan gum ⇄ psyllium husk [0.6oz (15g)]

bouillon cubes ⇄ vegetable broth [48floz (1.45L)]

MCT oil powder ⇄ neutral-flavored oil of choice [0.8floz (23ml)] and mayonnaise [1.0floz (30ml)]

TVP ⇄ fresh plant-based ground/mince [1 pound (454g)] (e.g. Impossible or Beyond Meat) for the Hearty Homestyle Chili and 8 Beyond Breakfast Sausage links, or similar product, to replace the Bacony Bits on salads (half a link = 1 serving of Bacony Bits)

Notes & Tips

*Two recipes in the meal plan involve toasting **pumpkin seeds**. Feel free to buy 4.7oz (133g) toasted seeds and 17oz (480g) untoasted.*

***Agar agar powder** can be omitted from the recipe. The results will be a little wetter and slightly less eggy in texture, but still very tasty.*

*You may wish to blend fortified and unfortified **nutritional yeast** to avoid overconsuming certain micronutrients.*

***Parchment liners** are not needed if you have a silicone tin or liners.*

*Feel free to buy any 0g net carb flavor of **seaweed snacks** you enjoy.*

*If not using **shirataki noodles**, you will be making a soup that requires an additional 0.5floz (15ml) each of sesame oil, tamari (or soy sauce or aminos), and lemon or lime juice.*

*If you prefer to buy canned **soybeans** (e.g. Eden black soybeans), this is equivalent to six 15-ounce (425g) cans of beans, or a total of 55oz (1,548g) of cooked/canned beans. Be aware that, according to label data, canned/jarred soybeans contain more net carbs than what national data suggests are present in soybeans cooked from dried.*

*Pea-based **TVP** isn't easy to come by everywhere. In the UK, Profusion makes a pea and fava TVP mince that has okay macros.*

***Chili powder** and **pumpkin spice** are common North American spice blends. You can find recipes on page 78 if needed.*

***Kala namak** creates an eggy flavor in some of the dishes. However, if it's not available to you, regular salt can be used in its place.*

*Using regular **dark chocolate** will increase the net carbs somewhat.*

THE SHOPPING LIST: **perishable items**

The perishable shopping list is uniquely structured to allow for shopping flexibility. This list, as well as more traditionally structured weekly shopping lists, can be found at keto4vegans.com/resources.

Ingredients that appear more than once in the meal plan recipes are displayed in the chart below, while items that appear only once are listed separately at the top of the righthand page. On the chart, days that include items listed separately are highlighted.

Given weights are for edible food components only, unless noted overwise (●). When shopping, take into account that items may need to be trimmed or peeled, and spoiled portions discarded.

👓C beware of high-carb products ✎ see notes ⟳ ingredient swap available ● this weight includes the inedible components

DAY	1	2	3	4	5	6	7	8	9	10	11	12	13	14	15	16	17
avocado, medium [≈ 7 oz (200g) ● each]			1/2	1/2									1/2	1/2			
basil (0.42oz = 12g)									.42		✎						
carrots, medium [≈ 2.3oz (64g) each]			1			2					1						
cauliflower [a medium head ≈ 20oz (558g)]						21oz ✎ 585g									11oz 321g		
celery [a head ≈ 16oz (454g)] ✎	30oz 860g										1.4oz 40g						
cucumber, English, medium [≈ 10.6oz (300g)]																	
garlic, cloves (10 to 12 cloves per bulb)	3		3	4		8				3	2		4		1		3
ginger, a 1" (2.5cm) square piece [≈ 0.66 oz (19g)]						1											1/2
green onions, medium stalk [≈ 0.53oz (15g) each]						2 ⟳											
lemons, medium [≈ 1.6floz (45ml) of juice each] ✎	1 1/2		1/2	1					1/2				1				
mixed greens, baby leaves								10oz 285g							9.5oz 270g		
mushrooms, white button	8oz 227g		8oz 227g			8oz 227g					4oz 113g						
onions, medium [≈ 3.9oz (110g) each]	1/4		1			1/2					1/2				1/4 ✎		1/2
parsley, a bunch [≈ 2oz (56g)]						1/4 ⟳											
raspberries																	
red bell pepper, medium [≈ 5.3oz (150g) ● each]	1	1/2	1		1/2	1											
spinach, baby leaves			13oz 360g			4.2oz 120g					2.1oz 60g		11oz 300g				
strawberries							15oz | 420g										
tomatoes, medium [≈ 4.3oz (123g) each]																	
zucchini [total of 8oz (226g), about 1 medium]											2.1oz 60g			5.9oz 166g			
soy or **pea milk**, liters or 32-ounce cartons 👓C	2				2					2							
tofu, extra-firm [total of 2 × 4-serving blocks] ✎																	
DAY	1	2	3	4	5	6	7	8	9	10	11	12	13	14	15	16	17

Day 6: green beans - 4.2oz (120g)

Day 13: buttery spread - 1.3oz (37g)

Day 15: broccoli, florets - 11oz (319g), about 1 small crown

Day 23: chives - 0.2oz (6g)
dill - a sprig
lettuce, Romaine - 20oz (570g), about 1 medium head or 3 to 4 hearts

Day 26: cabbage, green, shredded - 20oz (560g), about 1/2 medium-large head

Day 34: alfalfa sprouts - 1.5oz (43g)
bok choy, baby - 3 heads [10oz (294g)]
radishes - 2oz (56g), about 1/2 bunch

19	20	21	22	23	24	25	26	27	28	29	30	31	32	33	34	35
1/2	1/2	1/2	1/2	1/4	1/4	1/2						1/2	1/2		1	
									.42							
1															1	
✎																
1/2				1/4	1/4											
1				4			1	1								
2							2								1	
1 1/2				1/2				1/2	1/2						1/2	
		2.1oz 60g						6.3oz 180g					6.3oz 180g			
															4oz 113g	
1																
				8oz 227g			4.3oz 123g			11oz 308g						
				1/2	1/2					1/2		1/2				
4.2oz 120g																
3/4		3/4	1/2													
			2							3						
				6oz 170g			18oz 510g									
19	20	21	22	23	24	25	26	27	28	29	30	31	32	33	34	35

Ingredient Swaps

Day 6: fresh parsley ⇄ dried parsley

Day 6 and Day 19: green onions ⇄ 1/4 medium [1.0oz (28g)] onion, preferably red

Day 23: fresh chives ⇄ dried chives or half of a green onion top

Day 23: fresh dill ⇄ dried dill

Notes & Tips

Day 1: *celery bought for Days 1 to 5 may, or may not, last until Day 11.*

Day 6: *the green onion adds a fresh touch to the Kung Pao Beans on Cauli-Hemp Rice. However, for shopping ease, normal onion could be used instead.*

Day 6 (& Day 19): *this cauliflower will be made into rice and a portion will be frozen for use on Day 19. If you prefer to buy premade cauliflower rice, you will need 2 1/2 cups [12oz (325g)] cooked rice on Day 6 and 2 cups [9.2oz (260g)] on Day 19. Uncooked cauliflower may weigh slightly less once cooked.*

Day 11: *leftover basil leaves can be added to the Minestrone with negligible affect on macros.*

Day 15: *the onion in the recipe is preferably red onion, but white or yellow onion can be used.*

Day 23: *tofu is typically packed in water. The weight here, and the weight on the package, is the drained/pressed weight. By my estimates, the unpressed weight of this much tofu would be about 30oz (840g).*

Day 26: *feel free to use a coleslaw mix that contains some carrot and red cabbage.*

Lemons *and* ***soy/pea milk*** *have been rounded to the nearest half lemon and half liter/quart (i.e. 32-ounces).*

Fresh herbs *and* ***alfalfa sprouts*** *are very low in net carbs. Leftovers can be added to other dishes with negligible affect on macros.*

Meal Plan week 1

	Day 1	Day 2	Day 3
	Breakfast ☐ **Pumpkin Spice Chia Pudding (×2)** | Page 20 | **Lunch** ☐ **Soybean Hummus (×2.5)** | Page 68 | ☐ Veggie sticks: ▸ 3 1/2 medium stalks (140g) celery ▸ 3/4 medium (89g) red bell pepper **Dinner** ☐ **Cream of Mushroom Soup** | Page 32 | ☐ **Hemp & Pumpkin Seed Crackers (×2)** | Page 30 | **Add-ons** ☐ 1 cup (240ml) soy or pea milk ☐ a packet (5g) seaweed snacks **Notes** *Pumpkin Spice Chia Pudding:* *Two servings is half the batch, roughly 2 cups or 458g.* *Refrigerate the leftover coconut milk and pumpkin purée in well-sealed airtight containers. They will be used on Day 5 and Day 6.* *Soybean Hummus:* *2.5 servings is a quarter of the full recipe, roughly 1/2 cup + 2 tablespoons or 158g.* *Assuming you are cooking soybeans from dry, I'd suggest making enough for the full meal plan now rather than recipe by recipe. Two thirds of the beans, 6 cups [36oz (1,032g)] worth, will be used this week. I suggest then freezing the remaining 3 cups worth in two separate 1 1/2 cup (258g) portions for use on Days 11 and 17.*	**Breakfast** ☐ Pumpkin Spice Chia Pudding (×2) **Lunch** ☐ Soybean Hummus (×2.5) ☐ Veggie sticks: ▸ 4 medium stalks (160g) celery ▸ 1/2 medium (60g) red bell pepper **Dinner** ☐ Cream of Mushroom Soup ☐ Hemp & Pumpkin Seed Crackers (×2) **Add-ons** ☐ 1 cup (240ml) soy or pea milk ☐ a packet (5g) seaweed snacks **Notes** *None.* **Day 1 Notes cont.** *Cream of Mushroom Soup:* *If you're not a mushroom fan, I'd suggest making the Cream of Broccolini Soup in its place to maintain similar daily macros.*	**Breakfast** ☐ **Carrot Cake Breakfast Bars (×2)** | Page 22 | **Lunch** ☐ Cream of Mushroom Soup ☐ Hemp & Pumpkin Seed Crackers (×2) ☐ Simple salad: ▸ 2 cups (60g) spinach ▸ **MCT Ranch Dressing (×2)** | Page 70 | **Dinner** ☐ **Hearty Homestyle Chili** | Page 48 | ☐ 1/2 medium (68g) avocado **Add-ons** ☐ 1 cup (240ml) soy or pea milk ☐ a packet (5g) seaweed snacks **Notes** *Carrot Cake Breakfast Bars:* *Freeze 2 bars for a future meal.* *Hearty Homestyle Chili:* *I like to cut up the avocado and put it on top of the chili.* *Freeze 9 portions of chili in separate containers. 7 of these will be used for future meals. You will have 2 left over for use post meal plan.* *Tomato paste will be used again on Day 11 (Multi-Option Minestrone - 2 tablespoons [33g]) and Day 17 (Bean & Pumpkin Curry Patties - 1 tablespoon [16g]). Depending on the size and use-by date of your product, you may wish to freeze these portions for future use in these recipes.*
Legend (×2) eat two servings, etc. make this recipe well in advance/this recipe includes components that require advanced preparation long preparation, baking, or cooling time make a half batch make a double batch freeze thaw	**Nutritional Information** 1,722 calories | 80g protein 125g fat | 28g net carbs	**Nutritional Information** 1,717 calories | 80g protein 125g fat | 27g net carbs	**Nutritional Information** 1,652 calories | 83g protein 125g fat | 26g net carbs

Day 4

Breakfast
- ☐ Carrot Cake Breakfast Bars (×2)

Lunch
- ☐ Soybean Hummus (×2.5)
- ☐ 5 medium stalks (200g) celery, cut into sticks
- ☐ 1/2 medium (68g) avocado

Dinner
- ☐ **Lemon Garlic Spinach** | Page 36 |
- ☐ Hemp & Pumpkin Seed Crackers (×2)

Add-ons
- ☐ 1 cup (240ml) soy or pea milk
- ☐ a packet (5g) seaweed snacks

Notes
<u>*Lunch (re: avocado):*</u>

The avocado is allocated to lunch for the sake of calorie balance. However, it would also be nice mashed up with salt and used to top the crackers included with dinner.

<u>*Lemon Garlic Spinach:*</u>

For help halving the recipe, refer to the chart on page 100.

Nutritional Information
1,727 calories | 79g protein
136g fat | 27g net carbs

Day 5

Breakfast
- ☐ **Pumpkin Spice Chia Pudding (×2)** | Page 20 |

Lunch
- ☐ Soybean Hummus (×2.5)
- ☐ Veggie sticks:
  - 4 medium stalks (160g) celery
  - 1/2 medium (60g) red bell pepper

Dinner
- ☐ Lemon Garlic Spinach
- ☐ Hemp & Pumpkin Seed Crackers (×2)

Add-ons
- ☐ 1 cup (240ml) soy or pea milk
- ☐ a packet (5g) seaweed snacks

Notes
<u>*Pumpkin Spice Chia Pudding:*</u>

Two servings is half the batch, roughly 2 cups or 458g.

You'll need 1/2 cup (123g) of pumpkin purée for tomorrow's Falafel-Inspired Breakfast Bars. You may wish to make sure your have this much remaining for that recipe and if necessary go scant on the pumpkin purée in the chia pudding. The purée is more structurally relevant to the outcome of the breakfast bar recipe.

Nutritional Information
1,714 calories | 78g protein
125g fat | 28g net carbs

Day 6

Breakfast
- ☐ Pumpkin Spice Chia Pudding (×2)

Lunch
- ☐ **Falafel-Inspired Breakfast Bars (×2)** | Page 80 |
- ☐ Simple salad:
  - 2 cups (60g) spinach
  - MCT Ranch Dressing (×2)

Dinner
- ☐ **Kung Pao Beans on Cauli-Hemp Rice** | Page 50 |

Add-ons
- ☐ 1 cup (240ml) soy or pea milk
- ☐ a packet (5g) seaweed snacks

Notes
<u>*Falafel-Inspired Breakfast Bars:*</u>

Use a 9-inch (23cm) square pan for a double batch of bars. Cut the bars into 12 and ❄ freeze 6 for future lunches.

For help with doubling the recipe, refer to the chart on page 100.

<u>*Kung Pao Beans on Cauli-Hemp Rice:*</u>

If you're making your own cauliflower rice, you can find guidance on page 76. The amount of cauliflower listed on Day 6 of the shopping list is to make rice for this recipe and the Unconventional Tabbouleh (Day 19). Therefore, if you're making your own rice, ❄ freeze a 2-cup (260g) portion for future use.

❄ You will have leftover Kung Pao-ish Sauce. Freeze a 1/4-batch portion (1/4 cup + 2 tablespoons [90ml]) for later use in the Coconut Kung Pao Noodle Bowl (Day 34). Store the remainder (1/2 cup + 2 tablespoons [150ml]) for use post meal plan.

Nutritional Information
1,652 calories | 83g protein
119g fat | 27g net carbs

Day 7

Breakfast
- ☐ **Crunchy Granola Bars (×2)** | Page 24 |
- ☐ 5 medium (60g) strawberries

Lunch
- ☐ Falafel-Inspired Breakfast Bars (×2)
- ☐ Simple salad:
  - 2 cups (60g) spinach
  - MCT Ranch Dressing (×2)

Dinner
- ☐ Kung Pao Beans on Cauli-Hemp Rice

Add-ons
- ☐ 1 cup (240ml) soy or pea milk
- ☐ a packet (5g) seaweed snacks

Notes
<u>*Crunchy Granola Bars:*</u>

The Granola Bars will be eaten throughout the meal plan, so make sure to dehydrate and cool them completely, and store them appropriately so they last. If you find the bars are becoming moist or stale, you can freshen them up in the oven for 30 to 45 minutes at 200°F (95°C). Fully cool them again if storing. You can also freeze the bars and thaw them as needed if you are concerned that they will not keep.

The crunchy bars have a long baking time, making soft cookies is another option. Bake cookies for today, tomorrow, and Day 10 and freeze the remaining cookies to thaw and bake as needed throughout the meal plan.

Nutritional Information
1,653 calories | 83g protein
128g fat | 27g net carbs

Meal Plan week 2

	Day 8	Day 9	Day 10
	Breakfast ☐ Crunchy Granola Bars (×2) ☐ 5 medium (60g) strawberries **Lunch** ☐ Falafel-Inspired Breakfast Bars (×2) ☐ Simple salad: ▸ 2 cups (60g) mixed greens ▸ MCT Ranch Dressing (×2) **Dinner** ☐ Kung Pao Beans on Cauli-Hemp Rice **Add-ons** ☐ 1 cup (240ml) soy or pea milk ☐ a packet (5g) seaweed snacks **Notes** *None.*	**Breakfast** ☐ ❄> Carrot Cake Breakfast Bars (×2) ☐ 5 medium (60g) strawberries **Lunch** ☐ Kung Pao Beans on Cauli-Hemp Rice **Dinner** ☐ **Mediterranean Fauxttata Bites (×3)** | Page 60 | ☐ Simple salad: ▸ 2 cups (60g) mixed greens ▸ MCT Ranch Dressing (×2) ▸ 1 tablespoon (10g) hemp hearts **Add-ons** ☐ 1 cup (240ml) soy or pea milk ☐ a packet (5g) seaweed snacks **Notes** *None.*	**Breakfast** ☐ Crunchy Granola Bars (×2) ☐ 5 medium (60g) strawberries **Lunch** ☐ Mediterranean Fauxttata Bites (×3) ☐ Simple salad: ▸ 1 1/2 cups (45g) mixed greens ▸ **Garlic Oregano Vinaigrette** | Page 70 | **Dinner** ☐ Kung Pao Beans on Cauli-Hemp Rice **Add-ons** ☐ 1 cup (240ml) soy or pea milk ☐ a packet (5g) seaweed snacks **Notes** *None.*
	Nutritional Information 1,650 calories | 82g protein 128g fat | 27g net carbs	**Nutritional Information** 1,580 calories | 84g protein 120g fat | 28g net carbs	**Nutritional Information** 1,581 calories | 79g protein 122g fat | 25g net carbs

Legend
(×2) eat two servings, etc.
make this recipe well in advance/this recipe includes components that require advanced preparation
◷ long preparation, baking, or cooling time
◐ make a half batch
◎ make a double batch
❄ freeze
❄> thaw

Day 11

Breakfast

- ☐ **Vanilla Coconut Chia Pudding (×2)** | Page 20 |
- ☐ 5 medium (60g) strawberries

Lunch

- ☐ Mediterranean Fauxttata Bites (×3)
- ☐ Simple salad:
  - 2 cups (60g) mixed greens
  - Garlic Oregano Vinaigrette (×1.5)

Dinner

- ☐ **Multi-Option Minestrone** | Page 34 |
- ☐ Hemp & Pumpkin Seed Crackers

Add-ons

- ☐ 1 cup (240ml) soy or pea milk
- ☐ a packet (5g) seaweed snacks

Notes

Vanilla Coconut Chia Pudding:

Two servings is half the batch, roughly 1 3/4 cups or 396g.

Refrigerate the remaining half-can of coconut milk in a well-sealed airtight container for use on Day 17.

Multi-Option Minestrone:

You'll be using carrot and zucchini for the vegetable options.

If you froze a 2-tablespoon (33g) portion of tomato paste for future use in this recipe, thaw it.

Thaw a 1 1/2 cup (258g) portion of soybeans for use in this recipe (if applicable).

Freeze 3 portions of soup in separate containers for future meals.

Refrigerate the remainder of the diced tomatoes in a well-sealed airtight container for later use in the Bean & Pumpkin Curry Patties recipe (Day 17).

Nutritional Information

1,656 calories | 78g protein
121g fat | 25g net carbs

Day 12

Breakfast

- ☐ Crunchy Granola Bars (×2)
- ☐ 5 medium (60g) strawberries

Lunch

- ☐ Mediterranean Fauxttata Bites (×3)
- ☐ Simple salad:
  - 2 cups (60g) mixed greens
  - Garlic Oregano Vinaigrette (×1.5)

Dinner

- ☐ Multi-Option Minestrone
- ☐ Hemp & Pumpkin Seed Crackers

Add-ons

- ☐ 1 cup (240ml) soy or pea milk
- ☐ a packet (5g) seaweed snacks

Notes

None.

Nutritional Information

1,661 calories | 78g protein
130g fat | 26g net carbs

Day 13

Breakfast

- ☐ Vanilla Coconut Chia Pudding (×2)
- ☐ 5 medium (60g) strawberries

Lunch

- ☐ Hearty Homestyle Chili
- ☐ 1/2 medium (68g) avocado

Dinner

- ☐ **Lemon Garlic Spinach** | Page 36 | with 3 tablespoons (30g) hemp hearts
- ☐ **Flax & Lupin Bread** | Page 28 | with 2 teaspoons vegan buttery spread

Add-ons

- ☐ 1 cup (240ml) soy or pea milk
- ☐ a packet (5g) seaweed snacks

Notes

Flax & Lupin Bread:

If using lupin flour in the bread recipe isn't an option for you, make the extra flaxseed meal and protein powder version to maintain similar macros.

Unless the bread is very fresh, i.e. only recently cooled, I like to toast it. Expect it to take longer to toast than most traditional breads.

Turn one third of the loaf (equal to 2 servings) into croutons for the Lupini Caesar Salad recipe you'll be making in Week 4. See the recipe page for instructions. Make sure to dehydrate and cool the croutons completely before sealing in an airtight container to ensure they keep until needed.

Nutritional Information

1,697 calories | 78g protein
124g fat | 26g net carbs

Day 14

Breakfast

- ☐ **Fudgy Zucchini Breakfast Bars (×2)** | Page 22 |

Lunch

- ☐ Hearty Homestyle Chili
- ☐ 1/2 medium (68g) avocado
- ☐ 1/4 cup (25g) walnuts

Dinner

- ☐ Lemon Garlic Spinach with 2 tablespoons (20g) hemp hearts
- ☐ Flax & Lupin Bread with 2 teaspoons vegan buttery spread

Add-ons

- ☐ 1 cup (240ml) soy or pea milk
- ☐ a packet (5g) seaweed snacks

Notes

Fudgy Zucchini Breakfast Bars:

Use a 9-inch (23cm) square pan for a double batch of bars. Cut the bars into 12 and freeze 6 for future breakfasts.

Refrigerate the leftover pumpkin purée in a well-sealed airtight container. It should last for up to a week and will be used up on Day 19.

Nutritional Information

1,711 calories | 77g protein
137g fat | 27g net carbs

Meal Plan **Week 3**

	Day 15	Day 16	Day 17
	Breakfast ☐ Fudgy Zucchini Breakfast Bars (×2) **Lunch** ☐ ❄➤ Multi-Option Minestrone ☐ Flax & Lupin Bread with 2 teaspoons vegan buttery spread ☐ Simple salad: ▸ 2 cups (60g) mixed greens ▸ Garlic Oregano Vinaigrette (×1.5) ▸ **Bacony Bits** | Page 72 ◷ | **Dinner** ☐ **Broccoli & Cauliflower Salad** | Page 38 | **Add-ons** ☐ 1 cup (240ml) soy or pea milk ☐ a packet (5g) seaweed snacks **Notes** _Bacony Bits:_ *These will be used throughout the meal plan. They appear in the Broccoli & Cauliflower Salad recipe and the Lupini Caesar Salad recipe as well as occasionally sprinkled on a simple salad to boost protein.* _Broccoli & Cauliflower Salad:_ *You will need to toast 1/3 cup (53g) pumpkin seeds again next week for the Spicy Cabbage Slaw (Day 26). You could toast those seeds now. Fully cool toasted seeds before storing.*	**Breakfast** ☐ Fudgy Zucchini Breakfast Bars (×2) **Lunch** ☐ ❄➤ Multi-Option Minestrone ☐ Flax & Lupin Bread with 2 teaspoons vegan buttery spread ☐ Simple salad: ▸ 2 cups (60g) mixed greens ▸ Garlic Oregano Vinaigrette (×1.5) ▸ Bacony Bits **Dinner** ☐ Broccoli & Cauliflower Salad **Add-ons** ☐ 1 cup (240ml) soy or pea milk ☐ a packet (5g) seaweed snacks **Notes** *None.*	**Breakfast** ☐ **Pumpkin Spice Chia Pudding (×2)** | Page 20 | **Lunch** ☐ Broccoli & Cauliflower Salad **Dinner** ☐ **Bean & Pumpkin Curry Patties (×2)** | Page 52 | fried in 2 teaspoons coconut oil ☐ Simple salad: ▸ 1 1/2 cups (45g) mixed greens ▸ Garlic Oregano Vinaigrette ▸ Bacony Bits **Add-ons** ☐ 1 cup (240ml) soy or pea milk ☐ a packet (5g) seaweed snacks **Notes** _Pumpkin Spice Chia Pudding:_ *Two servings is half the batch, roughly 2 cups or 458g.* *You'll need 1/2 cup (123g) of pumpkin purée for today's Bean & Pumpkin Curry Patties and 1/4 cup (61g) for tomorrow's Carrot Cake Breakfast Bars. You may wish to make sure you have this much remaining for those recipes and if necessary go scant on the pumpkin purée in the pudding.* _Bean & Pumpkin Curry Patties:_ ***You should have diced tomatoes left over from Day 11 for use in this recipe.*** *❄➤ Thaw the 1-tablespoon (16g) portion of tomato paste (if applicable).* *❄➤ Thaw a 1 1/2 cup (258g) portion of soybeans for use in this recipe (if applicable).* *❄ Freeze the remaining 280ml of coconut milk to be used in Week 5.* *❄ Freeze 4 patties for future meals.*
Legend (×2) eat two servings, etc. make this recipe well in advance/this recipe includes components that require advanced preparation ◷ long preparation, baking, or cooling time ◐ make a half batch ꝏ make a double batch ❄ freeze ❄➤ thaw			
	Nutritional Information 1,695 calories | 75g protein 134g fat | 28g net carbs	**Nutritional Information** 1,695 calories | 75g protein 134g fat | 28g net carbs	**Nutritional Information** 1,725 calories | 74g protein 130g fat | 27g net carbs

Day 18

Breakfast

☐ Pumpkin Spice Chia Pudding (×2)

Lunch

☐ Broccoli & Cauliflower Salad

Dinner

☐ Bean & Pumpkin Curry Patties (×2) fried in 2 teaspoons coconut oil

☐ Simple salad:

- 1½ cups (45g) mixed greens
- Garlic Oregano Vinaigrette
- Bacony Bits

Add-ons

☐ 1 cup (240ml) soy or pea milk

☐ a packet (5g) seaweed snacks

Notes

None.

Nutritional Information

1,725 calories | 74g protein

130g fat | 27g net carbs

Day 19

Breakfast

☐ **Carrot Cake Breakfast Bars (×2)**

| Page 22 |

Lunch

☐ ❄➤ Hearty Homestyle Chili

☐ ½ medium (68g) avocado

☐ Simple salad:

- 2 cups (60g) mixed greens
- Garlic Oregano Vinaigrette (×1.5)

Dinner

☐ **Unconventional Tabbouleh**

| Page 40 ◐ |

Add-ons

☐ 1 cup (240ml) soy or pea milk

☐ a packet (5g) seaweed snacks

Notes

<u>Unconventional Tabbouleh</u>:

You will be eating this tabbouleh for 4 days in a row, but I've suggested you make half a batch now and another half batch the day after tomorrow. This is because the veggies might not keep well for the full 4 days once chopped. However, the full batch of dressing can be prepared today as it will keep fine.

❄➤ If you froze a 2-cup (260g) portion of cauliflower rice on Day 6 for use in this recipe, thaw it.

Nutritional Information

1,662 calories | 77g protein

132g fat | 28g net carbs

Day 20

Breakfast

☐ Carrot Cake Breakfast Bars (×2)

Lunch

☐ Unconventional Tabbouleh

Dinner

☐ Bean & Pumpkin Curry Patties (×2) fried in 2 teaspoons coconut oil

☐ ½ medium (68g) avocado

Add-ons

☐ 1 cup (240ml) soy or pea milk

☐ a packet (5g) seaweed snacks

Notes

<u>Dinner (re: avocado)</u>:

I like to mash the avocado with some salt and put it atop the fried Bean & Pumpkin Curry Patties.

Nutritional Information

1,716 calories | 77g protein

139g fat | 26g net carbs

Day 21

Breakfast

☐ Carrot Cake Breakfast Bars (×2)

Lunch

☐ ❄➤ Hearty Homestyle Chili

☐ ½ medium (68g) avocado

☐ Simple salad:

- 2 cups (60g) mixed greens
- Garlic Oregano Vinaigrette (×1.5)

Dinner

☐ **Unconventional Tabbouleh**

| Page 40 ◐ |

Add-ons

☐ 1 cup (240ml) soy or pea milk

☐ a packet (5g) seaweed snacks

Notes

None.

Nutritional Information

1,662 calories | 77g protein

132g fat | 28g net carbs

Meal Plan week 4

Day 22

Breakfast

- ▢ Crunchy Granola Bars (×2)

Lunch

- ▢ ❄➤ Hearty Homestyle Chili
- ▢ 1/2 medium (68g) avocado
- ▢ 1/2 medium (62g) tomato

Dinner

- ▢ Unconventional Tabbouleh

Add-ons

- ▢ 1 cup (240ml) soy or pea milk
- ▢ a packet (5g) seaweed snacks

Notes

<u>*Lunch:*</u>

The tomato can be chopped and put atop the chili, or sliced and enjoyed with some salt and pepper. Another option is to make a little side salad of the tomato and avocado. Adding a splash of vinegar or lemon juice to the mixture would have little effect on the daily macros.

Nutritional Information

1,612 calories | 76g protein
127g fat | 26g net carbs

Day 23

Breakfast

- ▢ ❄➤ Fudgy Zucchini Breakfast Bar
- ▢ **Fruit-Tea Raspberry Smoothie** | Page 26 ⚘◷ |

Lunch

- ▢ **Eggy Tofu Salad** | Page 54 | on:
  - **Flax & Lupin Bread (×1.5)** | Page 28 ◐ ◷ |
  - 1/4 medium (75g) English cucumber, sliced
- ▢ 1/2 medium (60g) red bell pepper, cut into sticks

Dinner

- ▢ **Lupini Caesar Salad** | Page 42 |
- ▢ 1/4 medium (34g) avocado

Add-ons

- ▢ 1 cup (240ml) soy or pea milk
- ▢ a packet (5g) seaweed snacks

Notes

<u>*Fruit-Tea Smoothie*</u>:

Fruit-flavored tea ice cubes (optional) will need to be steeped and frozen the night before. You will make this smoothie again tomorrow, so you could make the cubes for both days.

<u>*Flax & Lupin Bread*</u>:

If you aren't able to use lupin flour, make the extra flaxseed meal and protein powder version of the bread to maintain similar macros.

Bake a half-batch loaf for 45 minutes.

Feel free to make a full batch of bread and freeze it or turn it into croutons for future use. However, keep in mind that the shopping list quantities only account for making half a batch.

Day 23 Notes cont.

<u>*Eggy Tofu Salad*</u>:

Don't top your bread with the Eggy Tofu Salad until you're ready to eat. It can become texturally unpleasant when wet.

If you purchased a 4-serving package of tofu, store the leftover portion fully submersed in water and refrigerated in an airtight container for use on Day 26.

<u>*Dinner (re: avocado):*</u>

The avocado can be chopped and put on the salad or enjoyed separately.

Nutritional Information

1,633 calories | 77g protein
122g fat | 27g net carbs

Day 24

Breakfast

- ▢ ❄➤ Fudgy Zucchini Breakfast Bar
- ▢ **Fruit-Tea Raspberry Smoothie** | Page 26 ⚘◷ |

Lunch

- ▢ Eggy Tofu Salad on:
  - Flax & Lupin Bread (×1.5)
  - 1/4 medium (75g) English cucumber, sliced
- ▢ 1/2 medium (60g) red bell pepper, cut into sticks

Dinner

- ▢ Lupini Caesar Salad with
- ▢ 1/4 medium (34g) avocado

Add-ons

- ▢ 1 cup (240ml) soy or pea milk
- ▢ a packet (5g) seaweed snacks

Notes

<u>*Fruit-Tea Smoothie*</u>:

See yesterday's notes.

Nutritional Information

1,633 calories | 77g protein
122g fat | 27g net carbs

Legend

(×2) eat two servings, etc.
⚘◷ make this recipe well in advance/this recipe includes components that require advanced preparation
◷ long preparation, baking, or cooling time
◐ make a half batch
ꝏ make a double batch
❄ freeze
❄➤ thaw

Day 25

Breakfast

- ☐ ❄➤ Fudgy Zucchini Breakfast Bars (×2)

Lunch

- ☐ ❄➤ Hearty Homestyle Chili
- ☐ 1/2 medium (68g) avocado

Dinner

- ☐ Lupini Caesar Salad
- ☐ **Hemp & Pumpkin Seed Crackers** | Page 30 ◐ ◷ |

Add-ons

- ☐ 1 cup (240ml) soy or pea milk
- ☐ a packet (5g) seaweed snacks

Notes

Hemp & Pumpkin Seed Crackers:

You will have one serving of crackers left over for use post meal plan.

Feel free to make a full batch of crackers and save some to enjoy post meal plan. However, keep in mind that the shopping list quantities only account for making half a batch.

Nutritional Information

1,579 calories | 77g protein
122g fat | 24g net carbs

Day 26

Breakfast

- ☐ Crunchy Granola Bars (×2)
- ☐ 1/2 cup (61g) raspberries

Lunch

- ☐ Lupini Caesar Salad
- ☐ Hemp & Pumpkin Seed Crackers

Dinner

- ☐ **Spicy Cabbage Slaw** | Page 44 |
- ☐ **Seasoned Air Fryer Tofu** | Page 56 |

Add-ons

- ☐ 1 cup (240ml) soy or pea milk
- ☐ a packet (5g) seaweed snacks

Notes

Seasoned Air Fryer Tofu:

As noted on the recipe page, the Seasoned Air Fryer Tofu can be baked in an oven.

Nutritional Information

1,709 calories | 80g protein
131g fat | 25g net carbs

Day 27

Breakfast

- ☐ Crunchy Granola Bars (×2)
- ☐ 1/2 cup (61g) raspberries

Lunch

- ☐ ❄➤ Falafel-Inspired Breakfast Bar (×2)
- ☐ Simple salad:
  - 1 cup (30g) mixed greens
  - **MCT Ranch Dressing** | Page 70 |

Dinner

- ☐ Spicy Cabbage Slaw
- ☐ Seasoned Air Fryer Tofu

Add-ons

- ☐ 1 cup (240ml) soy or pea milk
- ☐ a packet (5g) seaweed snacks

Notes

None.

Nutritional Information

1,636 calories | 79g protein
125g fat | 27g net carbs

Day 28

Breakfast

- ☐ ❄➤ Fudgy Zucchini Breakfast Bars (×2)

Lunch

- ☐ **Mediterranean Fauxttata Bites (×3)** | Page 60 |
- ☐ 1/4 cup (25g) walnuts
- ☐ Simple salad:
  - 1 cup (30g) mixed greens
  - MCT Ranch Dressing

Dinner

- ☐ Spicy Cabbage Slaw
- ☐ Seasoned Air Fryer Tofu

Add-ons

- ☐ 1 cup (240ml) soy or pea milk
- ☐ a packet (5g) seaweed snacks

Notes

Mediterranean Fauxttata Bites:

Feel free to make one of the variations on this recipe if you'd like to try something different. The variations are nutritionally similar and so daily macros won't be impacted greatly. However, keep in mind that the shopping list doesn't account for a change in ingredients.

Nutritional Information

1,636 calories | 81g protein
128g fat | 26g net carbs

Meal Plan **week 5**

	Day 29	Day 30	Day 31
	Breakfast ☐ Crunchy Granola Bars (×2) ☐ 1/2 cup (61g) raspberries	**Breakfast** ☐ Crunchy Granola Bars (×2) ☐ 1/2 cup (61g) raspberries	**Breakfast** ☐ **Vanilla Coconut Chia Pudding (×2)** | Page 20 | ☐ 1/2 cup (61g) raspberries
	Lunch ☐ Mediterranean Fauxttata Bites (×3) ☐ 1/2 medium (60g) red bell pepper, cut into sticks	**Lunch** ☐ Mediterranean Fauxttata Bites (×3) ☐ Simple salad: ▸ 2 cups (60g) mixed greens ▸ MCT Ranch Dressing (×2)	**Lunch** ☐ Mediterranean Fauxttata Bites (×3) ☐ 1/2 medium (60g) red bell pepper, cut into sticks
	Dinner ☐ ❄➤ Bean & Pumpkin Curry Patties (×2) fried in 2 teaspoons coconut oil ☐ Simple salad: ▸ 2 cups (60g) mixed greens ▸ MCT Ranch Dressing (×2)	**Dinner** ☐ Spicy Cabbage Slaw ☐ Seasoned Air Fryer Tofu	**Dinner** ☐ ❄➤ Bean & Pumpkin Curry Patties (×2) fried in 2 teaspoons coconut oil ☐ 1/2 medium (68g) avocado
	Add-ons ☐ 1 cup (240ml) soy or pea milk ☐ a packet (5g) seaweed snacks	**Add-ons** ☐ 1 cup (240ml) soy or pea milk ☐ a packet (5g) seaweed snacks	**Add-ons** ☐ 1 cup (240ml) soy or pea milk ☐ a packet (5g) seaweed snacks
Legend (×2) eat two servings, etc. make this recipe well in advance/this recipe includes components that require advanced preparation ◷ long preparation, baking, or cooling time ◐ make a half batch ꝏ make a double batch ❄ freeze ❄➤ thaw	**Notes** *None.*	**Notes** *None.*	**Notes** *Vanilla Coconut Chia Pudding:* *Two servings is half the batch, roughly 1 3/4 cups or 396g.* *Refrigerate the remaining half-can of coconut milk in a well-sealed airtight container for use on Day 34.*
	Nutritional Information 1,697 calories | 77g protein 133g fat | 27g net carbs	**Nutritional Information** 1,630 calories | 79g protein 124g fat | 26g net carbs	**Nutritional Information** 1,704 calories | 76g protein 125g fat | 26g net carbs

Day 32

Breakfast

☐ Vanilla Coconut Chia Pudding (×2)
☐ 1/2 cup (61g) raspberries

Lunch

☐ ❄> Falafel-Inspired Breakfast Bars (×2)
☐ Simple salad:
- 2 cups (60g) mixed greens
- MCT Ranch Dressing (×2)

Dinner

☐ ❄> Hearty Homestyle Chili
☐ 1/2 medium (68g) avocado

Add-ons

☐ 1 cup (240ml) soy or pea milk
☐ a packet (5g) seaweed snacks

Notes

None.

Nutritional Information
1,659 calories | 78g protein
119g fat | 27g net carbs

Day 33

Breakfast

☐ Crunchy Granola Bars (×2)
☐ 1/2 cup (61g) raspberries

Lunch

☐ ❄> Falafel-Inspired Breakfast Bars (×2)
☐ Simple salad:
- 2 cups (60g) mixed greens
- MCT Ranch Dressing (×2)

Dinner

☐ ❄> Multi-Option Minestrone
☐ Hemp & Pumpkin Seed Crackers

Add-ons

☐ 1 cup (240ml) soy or pea milk
☐ a packet (5g) seaweed snacks

Notes

None.

Nutritional Information
1,699 calories | 81g protein
131g fat | 28g net carbs

Day 34

Breakfast

☐ **Almond Joy Frappé** | Page 26 |

Lunch

☐ **Riced Edamame Rolls (×3)** | Page 62 |

Dinner

☐ **Coconut Kung Pao Noodle Bowl** | Page 58 |
☐ Hemp & Pumpkin Seed Crackers

Add-ons

☐ 1 cup (240ml) soy or pea milk
☐ a packet (5g) seaweed snacks

Notes

❄> *Thaw the leftover coconut milk from last week. Use this and the remaining half can from earlier in the week for the Coconut Kung Pao Noodle Bowl and today's and tomorrow's Almond Joy Frappés.*

Riced Edamame Rolls:

Construct the rolls only when ready to eat or the nori sheets will get gummy.

Coconut Kung Pao Noodle Bowl:

❄> *Defrost a 1/4-batch portion of Kung Pao-ish Sauce for use in this recipe.*

Feel free to make the soup variation of this dish if you cannot access, or do not like, shirataki noodles. However, be aware that you may find the noodle-free soup to be less filling.

There will be a serving of these noodles left over for use post meal plan.

Nutritional Information
1,644 calories | 82g protein
123g fat | 28g net carbs

Day 35

Breakfast

☐ **Almond Joy Frappé** | Page 26 |

Lunch

☐ Riced Edamame Rolls (×3)

Dinner

☐ Coconut Kung Pao Noodle Bowl
☐ Hemp & Pumpkin Seed Crackers

Add-ons

☐ 1 cup (240ml) soy or pea milk
☐ a packet (5g) seaweed snacks

Notes

None.

Nutritional Information
1,644 calories | 82g protein
123g fat | 28g net carbs

RECIPE MACRO & INGREDIENT **summary**

*Common allergens are **bolded** (in grey). Substitutions are given within the ingredient lists for items that appear infrequently. Otherwise, for frequently occurring items, the following substitutions can be made: almond butter ⇄ sunflower seed butter, almond extract - omitted, coconut milk ⇄ plant-based cooking cream, coconut oil ⇄ neutral-flavored oil of choice, soymilk ⇄ pea milk, tamari ⇄ coconut aminos, walnuts ⇄ sunflower seeds.*

The following ingredient substitutions can also be made to suit your preferences or access to certain products: allulose ⇄ granulated sweetener of choice (e.g. erythritol or erythritol blend), apple cider or rice vinegar ⇄ red/white wine vinegar, Dijon mustard ⇄ preferred mustard, Herbes de Provence ⇄ Italian seasoning, kala namak ⇄ normal salt, olive oil ⇄ neutral-flavored oil of choice, tamari ⇄ soy sauce or liquid aminos.

Note that, unless stated otherwise, herbs are dried versions and spices ground versions.

V - recipe **Variation** SF - soy-free version using **bold bean** option

MACROS / RECIPES	FULL RECIPE				SER	PER SERVING			
	CALS	PRO	FAT	NC		CALS	PRO	FAT	NC
Vanilla Coconut Chia Pudding	1,078	43	74	8.6	4	270	11	19	2.1
Pumpkin Spice Chia Pudding V	1,126	44	75	16	4	281	11	19	3.9
Chocolate Chia Pudding V	1,195	51	80	16	4	299	13	20	3.9
Golden Milk Chia Pudding V	1,117	44	75	15	4	279	11	19	3.6
Toffee Latté Chia Pudding V	1,100	44	75	12	4	275	11	19	3.0
Carrot Cake Breakfast Bars	1,415	66	114	22	6	236	11	19	3.6
Fudgy Zucchini Breakfast Bars V	1,411	64	117	22	6	235	11	19	3.6
Falafel-Inspired Breakfast Bars V	1,416	69	115	22	6	236	12	19	3.7
Crunchy Granola Bars/Soft Cookies	5,446	215	460	51	20	272	11	23	2.5
Almond Joy Frappé	539	33	41	9.2	1	539	33	41	9.2
Fruit-Tea Smoothie (Raspberry)	183	18	5.6	8.5	1	183	18	5.6	8.5
Flax & Almond Flour Bread	1,342	39	111	12	6	224	6.6	18	2.0
Flax & Chickpea Flour Bread	1,175	41	71	47	6	196	6.8	12	7.8
Flax & Lupin Flour Bread	1,049	57	71	7.7	6	175	9.4	12	1.3
Flax & Protein Powder Bread	1,235	60	87	5.4	6	206	10	15	0.9
Hemp & Pumpkin Seed Crackers	2,108	127	153	15	12	176	11	13	1.3
Cream of Asparagus Soup	632	18	53	12	3	211	6.0	18	4.1
Cream of Broccolini Soup	667	21	53	11	3	222	7.0	18	3.6
Cream of Celery Soup	613	14	53	10	3	204	4.8	18	3.3
Cream of Mushroom Soup	629	19	53	11	3	210	6.3	18	3.7
Cream of Zucchini Soup	626	16	53	13	3	209	5.3	18	4.3
Multi-Option Minestrone	1,253	67	86	37	5	251	13	17	7.4
Multi-Option Minestrone SF	1,191	44	64	73	5	238	8.8	13	15
Lemon Garlic Spinach	827	19	74	22	4	207	4.8	19	5.4

Vanilla Coconut Chia Pudding: allulose, chia seeds, **coconut milk** (full-fat, canned), vanilla extract, salt, **soymilk**. **Variations**: **Pumpkin Spice Chia Pudding** - pumpkin purée (canned), pumpkin spice; **Golden Milk Chia Pudding** - cinnamon, ginger (fresh), turmeric; **Chocolate Chia Pudding** - cocoa powder; **Toffee Latté Chia Pudding** - instant coffee, liquid stevia (toffee-flavored).

Carrot Cake Breakfast Bars: allulose, **almond butter**, baking powder, carrot, cinnamon, **coconut oil**, flaxseed meal, hemp hearts, nutmeg, nutritional yeast flakes, protein powder (vanilla), pumpkin purée (canned), salt, vanilla extract, **walnuts**. **Variations**: **Fudgy Zucchini Breakfast Bars** - cocoa powder, zucchini [omit carrot, cinnamon, and nutmeg]; **Falafel-Inspired Breakfast Bars** - black pepper, cardamon, coriander, crushed red pepper flakes, cumin, garlic (fresh and powder), parsley (fresh or dried), protein powder (plain pea), olive oil, onion (fresh and powder), **tamari** [omit allulose, coconut oil, cinnamon, nutmeg, protein powder (vanilla), and vanilla extract].

Crunchy Granola Bars/Soft Cookies: allulose, **almond butter**, **almond extract** (optional), baking powder, **Brazil nuts** or additional pumpkin seeds, chia seeds, chocolate chips, cinnamon, **coconut oil**, flaxseed meal, hemp hearts, nutritional yeast flakes, protein powder (vanilla), pumpkin seeds, salt, sesame seeds (brown or black), vanilla extract, **walnuts**.

Almond Joy Frappé: **almond butter**, **almond extract**, cocoa powder, **coconut milk** (full-fat, canned), protein powder (vanilla, chocolate, or coconut), **soymilk**.

Fruit-Tea Smoothie: berries (e.g. blackberries, raspberries, or strawberries), protein powder (vanilla or berry-flavored), **soymilk**, tea bag (berry-flavored - optional).

Flax & Fill-in-the-Blank Bread: baking powder, flaxseed meal, nutritional yeast flakes, olive oil, psyllium husks (whole), salt, vinegar (apple cider), xanthan gum (optional), and one of the following flours: **almond**, chickpea, **lupin**, **peanut** (defatted), protein powder (plain pea), or sesame seed (defatted).

Hemp & Pumpkin Seed Crackers: baking powder, black pepper, chia seeds, hemp hearts, Herbes de Provence, nutritional yeast flakes, olive oil, protein powder (plain pea), psyllium husks (whole), pumpkin seeds, salt. **Variation**: **Sesame & Pumpkin Seed Crackers** - sesame seeds (brown or black) [omit hemp hearts].

Cream of Vary-the-Vegetable Soup: bay leaf, bouillon cubes or vegetable broth, celery, crushed red pepper flakes, garlic, Herbes de Provence, **MCT oil powder** or additional olive oil, mushrooms (white), nutritional yeast flakes, olive oil, onion, red bell pepper, **soymilk**, **tamari**, Worcestershire sauce (optional), and one of the following main vegetables: asparagus, broccolini, celery, mushrooms, or zucchini.

Multi-Option Minestrone: bay leaf, black pepper, bouillon cubes or vegetable broth, celery, crushed red pepper flakes, cumin, garlic (fresh and powder), Herbes de Provence, mushrooms (white), nutritional yeast flakes, olive oil, onion (fresh and powder), oregano, **soybeans** or **cannellini beans**, spinach, thyme, tomatoes (canned, diced), tomato paste, either carrot or turnip, and one of the following: cauliflower, green beans, wax beans, or zucchini.

Lemon Garlic Spinach: garlic, lemon juice, olive oil, oregano, salt, spinach.

Broccoli & Cauliflower Salad: allulose, *Bacony Bits*, broccoli, cauliflower, garlic, mayonnaise, mustard (Dijon), nutritional yeast flakes, onion, pumpkin seeds, vinegar (apple cider), salt.

Unconventional Tabbouleh: cauliflower (riced or to rice), cucumber, garlic, green onions, hemp hearts, parsley (fresh), lemon juice, olive oil, olives (sliced, black), salt, sesame seeds (brown or black), spinach, tomato.

Lupini Caesar Salad: *Bacony Bits*, **Brazil nuts** or hemp hearts, ***Flax & Lupin Bread* croutons** or ones made with another variation of the *Flax & Fill-in-the-Blank Bread*, garlic, lemon juice, lettuce (Romaine), **lupini beans** (brined) or **soybeans** or pumpkin seeds, mayonnaise, mustard (Dijon), nutritional yeast flakes, olive oil, salt, **soymilk**.

MACROS / RECIPES	FULL RECIPE				SER	PER SERVING			
	CALS	PRO	FAT	NC		CALS	PRO	FAT	NC
Broccoli & Cauliflower Salad	1,817	72	148	33	4	454	18	37	8.4
Unconventional Tabbouleh	2,168	90	184	33	4	542	22	46	8.4
Lupini Caesar Salad	1,678	54	145	20	4	419	14	36	4.9
Spicy Cabbage Slaw	893	32	66	29	4	223	8.0	16	7.2
Spicy Bean & Bell Pepper Salad	1,445	85	101	31	4	361	21	25	7.7
Spicy Bean & Bell Pepper Salad SF	1,372	59	80	73	4	343	15	20	18
Hearty Homestyle Chili	2,778	201	169	77	10	278	20	17	7.7
Hearty Homestyle Chili SF	2,565	153	125	152	10	257	15	13	15
Kung Pao Beans on Cauli-Hemp Rice	1,949	126	137	40	5	390	25	27	7.9
Kung Pao Beans on Cauli-Hemp Rice SF	1,853	98	115	78	5	371	20	23	16
Bean & Pumpkin Curry Patties	1,925	106	141	38	10	193	11	14	3.8
Bean & Pumpkin Curry Patties SF	1,823	81	120	72	10	182	8.1	12	7.2
Eggy Tofu Salad	654	19	62	2.1	2	327	9.4	31	1.0
Seasoned Air Fryer Tofu	764	61	49	6.5	4	191	15	12	1.6
Coconut Kung Pao Noodle Bowl	784	21	62	21	3	261	7.1	21	7.1
Mediterranean Fauxttata Bites	1,658	86	131	22	12	138	7.1	11	1.9
Green Onion Curry Bites V	1,551	84	121	18	12	129	7.0	10	1.5
Faux-Sheesy Broccoli Bites V	1,622	91	122	23	12	135	7.6	10	1.9
Riced Edamame Rolls	1,091	42	84	16	6	182	7.0	14	2.7
Riced Lupini Rolls	1,087	47	80	22	6	181	7.8	13	3.6
Chickpea Risoni Rolls SF	1,201	40	79	55	6	200	6.7	13	9.2
Devilled Cucumber Slices	1,075	37	92	14	12	90	3.1	7.6	1.2
Kung Pao-ish Sauce	656	12	55	23	24	27	0.5	2.3	1.0
Soybean Hummus	1,731	75	145	28	10	173	7.5	15	2.8
Lupini Hummus	1,525	58	128	33	10	153	5.8	13	3.3
Chickpea Hummus SF	1,796	71	130	70	10	180	7.1	13	7.0
Garlic Oregano Vinaigrette	992	1.0	108	3.6	12	83	0.1	9.0	0.3
MCT Ranch Dressing	457	4.9	45	4.6	10	46	0.5	4.5	0.5
Bacony Bits	462	42	30	3.1	16	29	2.6	1.9	0.2
Green Eygg Pâté	1,041	68	72	12	8	130	8.5	9.1	1.5
Faux-Sheesy Jalapeño Pâté V	1,180	81	75	21	8	147	10	9.4	2.6
Shiitake Herb Pâté V	808	43	58	16	6	135	7.2	10	2.7

A more comprehensive summary can be downloaded from keto4vegans.com/resources.

Spicy Cabbage Slaw: allulose, black pepper, cabbage (green), green onions, garlic, mustard (Dijon), nutritional yeast flakes, olive oil or mayonnaise, oregano, pumpkin seeds, salt, sriracha, **tamari**, vinegar (red or white wine).

Spicy Bean & Bell Pepper Salad: allulose, bell peppers, black pepper, garlic, mustard (Dijon), nutritional yeast flakes, olive oil or mayonnaise, onion, oregano, pumpkin seeds, salt, **soybeans** or **pinto beans**, sriracha, **tamari**, vinegar (red or white wine).

Hearty Homestyle Chili: allulose, celery, chili powder, cocoa powder, cumin, garlic (fresh and powder), jalapeño slices (pickled), liquid smoke (optional), mushrooms (white), nutritional yeast flakes, olive oil, onion (fresh and powder), red bell pepper, salt, **soybeans** or **kidney beans**, tomatoes (canned, diced), tomato sauce (canned), tomato paste, TVP (preferably pea-based) or fresh plant-based ground/mince.

Kung Pao Beans on Cauli-Hemp Rice: cauliflower (riced or to rice), green beans, green onions, hemp hearts, *Kung Pao-ish Sauce*, mushrooms (white), **peanuts** (oil-roasted) or almonds (slivered) or pumpkin seeds, red bell pepper, **soybeans** or **black beans**.

Bean & Pumpkin Curry Patties: **coconut milk** (full-fat, canned), **coconut oil**, crushed red pepper flakes, curry powder, flaxseed meal, garam masala, garlic (fresh and powder), ginger (fresh), hemp hearts, nutritional yeast flakes, onion (fresh and powder), protein powder (plain pea), pumpkin purée (canned), salt, **soybeans** or **black beans**, **tamari**, tomatoes (canned, diced), tomato paste, **walnuts**.

Eggy Tofu Salad: black pepper, chives (fresh or dried), cumin, dill (fresh or dried), garlic, kala namak, mayonnaise, nutritional yeast flakes, paprika, **tofu** (extra-firm).

Seasoned Air Fryer Tofu: black pepper, cayenne pepper, cumin, garlic powder, nutritional yeast flakes, olive oil, onion powder, salt, **tamari**, **tofu** (extra-firm).

Coconut Kung Pao Noodle Bowl: bok choy, carrot, **coconut milk** (full-fat, canned), *Kung Pao-ish Sauce*, mushrooms (white), nutritional yeast flakes, sesame seeds (brown or black), shirataki noodles. **Variation**: **tamari**, sesame oil, lime juice [omit noodles].

Mediterranean Fauxttata Bites: baking powder, basil (fresh), black pepper, crushed red pepper flakes, cumin, garlic powder, hemp hearts, Herbes de Provence, kala namak, lemon juice, mustard (Dijon), nutritional yeast flakes, olive oil, olives (sliced, black), onion powder, paprika, protein powder (plain pea), pumpkin seeds, **soymilk**, tomatoes (sun-dried, in oil). **Variations**: [omit basil, olives, and sun-dried tomatoes] **Green Onion Curry Bites** - curry powder, garam masala, garlic, ginger (fresh), green onions; **Faux-Sheesy Broccoli Bites** - broccoli, liquid smoke (optional), onion, salt [omit kala namak].

Riced Edamame Rolls: alfalfa sprouts, allulose, avocado, chia seeds, **edamame** (frozen, shelled) or **lupini beans** or **chickpea risoni/rice**, garlic, green onion, lemon juice, lettuce (mixed greens) or microgreens, mayonnaise, radishes, nori (sushi sheets), salt, sesame seeds (brown or black), sriracha, vinegar (rice).

Devilled Cucumber Slices: black pepper, cucumber, *Green Eygg Pâté*, kala namak, mayonnaise, mustard (Dijon).

Kung Pao-ish Sauce: allulose, black pepper, coriander (the spice - optional), cornstarch, crushed red pepper flakes, garlic, ginger (fresh), onion, **tamari**, sesame oil, vinegar (rice).

Soybean Hummus: cumin, garlic, lemon juice, nutritional yeast flakes, olive oil, salt, **soybeans** or **lupini beans** or **chickpeas**, **soymilk**, tahini.

Garlic Oregano Vinaigrette: allulose, black pepper, garlic, mustard (Dijon), olive oil, oregano, vinegar (red or white wine).

MCT Ranch Dressing: black pepper, dill, garlic (fresh and powder), lemon juice, mayonnaise, **MCT oil powder** or additional mayonnaise, nutritional yeast flakes, onion powder, parsley, salt, **soymilk**, vinegar (apple cider), Worcestershire sauce (optional).

Bacony Bits: cumin, garlic powder, liquid smoke (optional), liquid stevia (preferably maple), nutritional yeast flakes, olive oil, paprika, **tamari**, TVP (preferably pea-based).

Green Eygg Pâté: agar agar, garlic powder, kala namak, nutritional yeast flakes, onion powder, pumpkin seeds. **Variations**: [omit kala namak] **Sheesy Jalapeño Pâté** - cumin, jalapeño slices (pickled), lemon juice, **miso paste**; **Shiitake Herb Pâté** - crushed red pepper flakes, garlic, Herbes de Provence, mushrooms (shiitake), olive oil, onion, **tamari**.

HELPFUL **divisions & conversions**

MEASUREMENT MANIPULATIONS

Ingredient quantities in recipes are typically given in both American cup/spoon measurements and either gram or milliliter measurements. Occasionally ounces are used. Doubling or dividing gram or milliliter quantities is quite straightforward. However, adjusting cup and spoon measurements can be more of a mathematical challenge. This chart does the math for you.

To save space, tablespoon and teaspoon are abbreviated to Tbsp and tsp.

CUP & SPOON MEASUREMENT	EQUIVALENTS			MEASUREMENT MULTIPLICATION & DIVISION			
	ML	FLUID OUNCES	SPOONS	double	halve	third	quarter
1 cup	240	8	16 Tbsp	2 cups	$\frac{1}{2}$ cup	$\frac{1}{3}$ cup	$\frac{1}{4}$ cup
$\frac{3}{4}$ cup	180	6	12 Tbsp	$1\frac{1}{2}$ cup	$\frac{1}{4}$ cup + 2 Tbsp	$\frac{1}{4}$ cup	3 Tbsp
$\frac{2}{3}$ cup	160	5.3	10 Tbsp + 2 tsp	$1\frac{1}{3}$ cup	$\frac{1}{3}$ cup	$3\frac{1}{2}$ Tbsp	2 Tbsp + 2 tsp
$\frac{1}{2}$ cup	120	4	8 Tbsp	1 cup	$\frac{1}{4}$ cup	2 Tbsp + 2 tsp	2 Tbsp
$\frac{1}{3}$ cup	80	2.7	5 Tbsp + 1 tsp	$\frac{2}{3}$ cup	2 Tbsp + 2 tsp	1 Tbsp + 2 tsp	1 Tbsp + 1 tsp
$\frac{1}{4}$ cup	60	2	4 Tbsp	$\frac{1}{2}$ cup	2 Tbsp	1 Tbsp + 1 tsp	1 Tbsp
$\frac{1}{8}$ cup	30	1	2 Tbsp	$\frac{1}{4}$ cup	1 Tbsp	2 tsp	$1\frac{1}{2}$ tsp
1 Tbsp	15	0.5	3 tsp	2 Tbsp	$1\frac{1}{2}$ tsp	1 tsp	$\frac{1}{2}$ + $\frac{1}{4}$ tsp
1 tsp	5	-	-	2 tsp	$\frac{1}{2}$ tsp	heaped $\frac{1}{4}$ tsp	$\frac{1}{4}$ tsp
$\frac{1}{2}$ tsp	2.5	-	-	1 tsp	$\frac{1}{4}$ tsp	heaped $\frac{1}{8}$ tsp	$\frac{1}{8}$ tsp
$\frac{1}{4}$ tsp	1.3	-	-	$\frac{1}{2}$ tsp	$\frac{1}{8}$ tsp	scant $\frac{1}{8}$ tsp	$\frac{1}{16}$ tsp
$\frac{1}{8}$ tsp	0.6	-	-	$\frac{1}{4}$ tsp	$\frac{1}{16}$ tsp (a pinch)	-	$\frac{1}{32}$ tsp (a smidgen)

NOTES & TIPS

$\frac{1}{2}$ tablespoon is equal to $1\frac{1}{2}$ teaspoons

The United States is not the only country that uses cups. Some countries may use a metric cup, which is 250ml, as opposed to 240ml. Depending on the ingredient, this 10ml difference could impact the outcome of a recipe.

If you don't have a set of spoons that measures below $\frac{1}{8}$ teaspoon, simply half or quarter fill the $\frac{1}{8}$ spoon to divide this measurement.

INGREDIENT WEIGHTS

In the recipes, gram and milliliter measurements are only given for quantities of 1 tablespoon and above. In addition, both gram <u>and</u> milliliter measurements are only provided for an ingredient if the difference equals or exceeds 5 units of measure. Thus, for those who prefer to weigh all of their ingredients, this chart provides the weight equivalents for items that often appear in the recipes, but for which a gram measurement may not have been provided.

INGREDIENT	1 teaspoon	1 tablespoon	$1\frac{1}{2}$ tablespoons	2 tablespoons
mayonnaise	4.5g	14g	21g	27.5g
oil	4.5g	13.5g	20g	27g
sriracha	6g	18.5g	28g	37g
tamari / soy sauce	6g	18g	27g	36g
garlic, crushed	6g	18g	-	-
ginger, grated or paste	6g	18g	-	-
nut/seed butter	5.5g	16g	24g	32g
tomato paste	5.5g	16.5g	25g	33g
agar agar powder	3g	-	-	-
baking powder or soda	4.5g	14g	-	-
herbs, dried	1g	3g	-	-
salt	6g	18g	-	-
spices, ground	2.5g	7.5g	-	-

NOTES & TIPS

Weights for herbs, spices, and nut/seed butters are averages. There is slight variation by type. For tahini, gram and milliliter measurements are equivalent.

Numbers have been rounded to the nearest 0.5g.

Made in the USA
Coppell, TX
02 February 2024